The
Bridge World's

TEST YOUR PLAY

PROBLEM 1

Rubber bridge
Neither vulnerable

North
♠ 5 4
♡ K Q 10
◇ K 5 2
♣ A K 8 5 4

South
♠ 7 3 2
♡ A J 7
◇ A Q 9 8 6 4
♣ 3

W	N	E	S
			1◇
1♠	2♣	2♠	pass
pass	3♠	pass	4◇
pass	5◇	all pass	

Trick 1: ♠K, ♠4, ♠10, ♠2. Trick 2: ♠A, ♠5, ♠8, ♠3. Trick 3: ♠Q, ◇5, ♠6, ♠7. Trick 4: ◇4, ♡2, ◇K, ◇3. Plan the play.

PROBLEM 2

Rubber bridge
North-South vulnerable

North
♠ 4 2
♡ A K 5
◇ J 9 7
♣ J 7 6 3 2

South
♠ A K Q 9
♡ Q 10
◇ A K Q 4
♣ A 5 4

W	N	E	S
			2♣
pass	2◇	pass	2NT
pass	4NT	pass	6NT
all pass			

West leads the ♠J. Plan the play.

PROBLEM 3

Rubber bridge
Both vulnerable

North
- ♠ A K
- ♡ A Q J 10
- ◇ Q J 10 9
- ♣ 9 5 4

South
- ♠ —
- ♡ 9 8
- ◇ A 4 3
- ♣ A K Q J 10 8 7 6

W	N	E	S
			1♣
pass	1♡	pass	3♣
pass	4NT	pass	7♣
all pass			

West leads the ♠Q. Plan the play.

PROBLEM 4

Rubber bridge
Neither vulnerable

North
- ♠ Q 7
- ♡ Q 8 2
- ◇ A J 9 6
- ♣ A K Q 2

South
- ♠ A 8 6
- ♡ K 6
- ◇ K Q 10
- ♣ J 9 7 4 3

W	N	E	S
			1♣
1♡	2♡	pass	2NT
pass	6♣	all pass	

West leads the ◇2.
(a) Plan the play.
(b) Plan the play at 6NT.

PROBLEM 5

Rubber bridge
North-South vulnerable

North
♠ 7 6 5
♡ 8 6 5
◇ 7 6 4
♣ A K J 3

South
♠ A Q J 8 4 2
♡ A Q J
◇ A K
♣ 8 7

W	N	E	S
			2♣
pass	2◇	pass	2♠
pass	3♠	pass	4◇
pass	5♣	pass	5♡
pass	6♣	pass	6♠
all pass			

West leads the ♣2. Plan the play.

PROBLEM 6

Rubber bridge
Both vulnerable

North
♠ 3
♡ A K
◇ K 10 8 3
♣ A K 8 6 4 3

South
♠ K 8 7 6 5 4
♡ Q
◇ A Q J 9
♣ 7 5

W	N	E	S
			1♠
pass	2♣	pass	2◇
pass	4NT	pass	5◇
pass	6◇	all pass	

Trick 1: ♠Q, ♠3, ♠A, ♠4. Trick 2: ◇2, ?. Plan the play.

PROBLEM 7

Rubber bridge
Neither vulnerable

North
- ♠ 3
- ♡ K Q 6
- ◇ 8 6 4 3
- ♣ A K 6 5 2

South
- ♠ Q 7
- ♡ A J 10 4
- ◇ A K 7
- ♣ 9 8 7 3

W	N	E	S
pass	1♣	pass	1♡
1♠	2♡	pass	4♡
all pass			

Trick 1: ♠K, ♠3, ♠2, ♠7. Trick 2: ◇Q, ◇3, ◇10, ?.
Plan the play.

PROBLEM 8

IMPs
North-South vulnerable

North
- ♠ A Q 10
- ♡ J 8 7
- ◇ K 5 3 2
- ♣ A 5 3

South
- ♠ K J 6
- ♡ A K 9
- ◇ A J 9 8 4
- ♣ K 6

W	N	E	S
			1◇
pass	2◇	pass	3NT
pass	4NT	pass	6◇
all pass			

West leads the ♣J. Plan the play.

Rubber bridge
East-West vulnerable

North
♠ J 10 6
♡ J 9 7 5
◇ A K 4 2
♣ A 5

South
♠ 5 3
♡ A K 4 2
◇ Q 7
♣ K Q J 6 2

W	N	E	S
1♠	pass	pass	dbl
pass	2♠	pass	3♡
pass	4♡	all pass	

Trick 1: ♠K, ♠6, ♠2, ♠3. Trick 2: ♠Q, ♠10, ♠7, ♠5. Trick 3: ♠A, ♠J, ♠9, ♡2.
Trick 4: ♡A, ♡3, ♡5, ♡8. Trick 5: ♡K, ♡6, ♡7, ◇3. Plan the play.

Rubber bridge
North-South vulnerable

North
♠ A K J 2
♡ Q 10
◇ 7 6 4 3
♣ 9 8 5

South
♠ 7 3
♡ A K J 9 5 4
◇ A K 5 2
♣ A

W	N	E	S
		2♠[1]	dbl
pass	2NT	pass	4♡
pass	6♡	all pass	
	1. Weak.		

West leads the ♠8. Plan the play.

PROBLEM 11

Rubber bridge
North-South vulnerable

North
♠ 4 3 2
♡ A K 4 3
◊ 7 5 4
♣ K 4 3

South
♠ K 8 6
♡ 10 9 7 5
◊ A K J
♣ A 8 6

W	N	E	S
			1NT
pass	2♣	2♠	pass
pass	2NT	pass	3♡
pass	4♡	all pass	

Trick 1: ♠5, ♠2, ♠A, ♠6. Trick 2: ♠Q, ♠K, ♡6, ♠3. Trick 3: ♡8, ♡K, ♡2, ♡5.
Trick 4: ♡A, ♡Q, ♡7, ♡J.
(a) Plan the play.
(b) Plan the play if the contract is 3♡.

PROBLEM 12

Rubber bridge
East-West vulnerable

North
♠ 5 4
♡ K Q 3 2
◊ K Q 6 2
♣ K J 7

South
♠ A K 9 8
♡ A 8 6
◊ A 5 3
♣ A Q 10

W	N	E	S
			2NT
pass	6NT	all pass	

West leads the ♠Q. East plays the ♣2. Plan the play.

PROBLEM 13

Rubber bridge
Neither vulnerable

North
- ♠ A 6
- ♡ Q J 5 2
- ◇ K 10 8 7
- ♣ 9 4 3

South
- ♠ 5 3
- ♡ A K 10 9 4
- ◇ A 6 4
- ♣ A K Q

W	N	E	S
			2NT
pass	3♣	pass	3♡
pass	5♡	pass	6♡
all pass			

West leads the ♠4. Plan the play.

PROBLEM 14

Rubber bridge
East-West vulnerable

North
- ♠ A Q J 5 2
- ♡ A 7
- ◇ Q 7
- ♣ A 8 6 4

South
- ♠ 10 7
- ♡ K Q 9 8
- ◇ A J 6 5 4 2
- ♣ 3

W	N	E	S
			1◇
pass	1♠	pass	2◇
pass	3♣	pass	3NT
pass	4◇	pass	5◇
pass	6◇	all pass	

Trick 1: ♠6, ♠2, ♠K, ♠7. Trick 2: ♠4, ♠10, ♠3, ?. Plan the play.

PROBLEM 15

IMPs
East-West vulnerable

North
♠ A K 7
♡ K 10
◇ A 7 4 2
♣ A J 8 3

South
♠ J 6 2
♡ A Q 9
◇ K 8 5
♣ K Q 7 4

W	N	E	S
			1♣
pass	2NT	pass	3NT
pass	4♣	pass	6♣
all pass			

Trick 1: ♣2, ♣3, ♣10, ♣Q. Trick 2: ♣4, ♣5, ♣A, ♡3. Plan the play.

PROBLEM 16

Rubber bridge
East-West vulnerable

North
♠ A 9 6 4
♡ Q 10
◇ K J 8
♣ 7 5 3 2

South
♠ K J 7
♡ 3
◇ A Q 10 9 6 5 4 2
♣ 8

W	N	E	S
			5◇
all pass			

Trick 1: ♣K, ♣2, ♣6, ♣8. Trick 2: ♣A, ♣3, ♣J, ?.
Plan the play.

PROBLEM 17

Rubber bridge
Neither vulnerable

North
- ♠ 7 5 4
- ♡ Q 8 5
- ◇ K 8 5 4 2
- ♣ J 6

South
- ♠ Q J 10
- ♡ A 10 9 6 4 2
- ◇ A
- ♣ A Q 5

W	N	E	S
		1NT[1]	dbl
2♣	pass	pass	2♡
pass	3♡	pass	4♡
all pass			
1.	15-17.		

Trick 1: ♠2, ♠4, ♠K, ♠10. Trick 2: ♠A, ♠J, ♠3, ♠5.
Trick 3: ♠6, ♠Q, ♠8, ♠7. Plan the play.

PROBLEM 18

Rubber bridge
East-West vulnerable

North
- ♠ 7 5 3 2
- ♡ Q 9 8
- ◇ 5 3 2
- ♣ A 10 7

South
- ♠ A K 6 4
- ♡ —
- ◇ A K Q J 10 6
- ♣ 8 6 2

W	N	E	S
			1◇
1♡	pass	3♡	3♠
4♡	4♠	all pass	

West leads the ♡J. Plan the play.

PROBLEM 19

Rubber bridge
East-West vulnerable

North
- ♠ A Q 5 2
- ♡ J 7
- ◇ A Q 9 2
- ♣ A 8 7

South
- ♠ J 7 6
- ♡ A Q 8
- ◇ —
- ♣ K 10 9 5 4 3 2

W	N	E	S
			1♣
pass	1♠	pass	2♣
pass	2◇	pass	2♠
pass	4♣	pass	4♡
pass	6♣	all pass	

West leads the ♣6. Plan the play.

PROBLEM 20

Rubber bridge
Both vulnerable

North
- ♠ 7 5 3
- ♡ A Q 6 4 2
- ◇ K 4 3
- ♣ K Q

South
- ♠ A 8 6
- ♡ 5
- ◇ A Q
- ♣ A 10 9 8 6 5 2

W	N	E	S
			1♣
pass	1♡	pass	3♣
pass	6♣	all pass	

West leads the ◇10. Plan the play.

PROBLEM 21

Rubber bridge
North-South vulnerable

North
- ♠ K 8 7 6
- ♡ A 9 6 3
- ◇ A K 3
- ♣ A 7

South
- ♠ A Q J 10 9 3
- ♡ K 2
- ◇ 7 5 4
- ♣ 8 6

W	N	E	S
	1◇	pass	1♠
pass	4♠	pass	4NT
pass	5◇¹	dbl	6♠
all pass			
	1. 1 or 4 key cards.		

West leads the ◇8. Plan the play.

PROBLEM 22

Rubber bridge
North-South vulnerable

North
- ♠ J 6 3
- ♡ 10 9 8
- ◇ Q 10 9 4
- ♣ K 10 3

South
- ♠ A Q 4 2
- ♡ 5
- ◇ A K J 6
- ♣ A Q J 6

W	N	E	S
			1◇
pass	1NT	pass	3♣
pass	3◇	pass	3♠
pass	4♠	all pass	

Trick 1: ♡K, ♡8, ♡6, ♡5. Trick 2: ♡3, ♡9, ♡A, ?. Plan the play.

PROBLEM 23

Rubber bridge
East-West vulnerable

North
- ♠ A 6 2
- ♡ Q J
- ◇ 9 8 7 5 4 3
- ♣ K 10

South
- ♠ K 10 9 5
- ♡ 8 3
- ◇ A
- ♣ A Q J 7 6 4

W	N	E	S
			1♣
pass	1◇	pass	1♠
pass	2♠	pass	3♠
pass	4♠	all pass	

Trick 1: ♡5, ♡J, ♡K, ♡3. Trick 2: ♡A, ♡8, ♡4, ♡Q.
Trick 3: ♡9, ♣4, ♡6, ♠2. Trick 4: ♠A, ♠4, ♠5, ♠3. Trick 5: ♠6, ♠7, ?.
Plan the play.

PROBLEM 24

Rubber bridge
Neither vulnerable

North
- ♠ K 8 6 2
- ♡ 6 5 4 3
- ◇ K Q
- ♣ 10 7 6

South
- ♠ A 5 4 3
- ♡ A 7 2
- ◇ 8 2
- ♣ A K Q J

W	N	E	S
			1♣
pass	1♡	pass	1♠
pass	2♠	pass	4♠
all pass			

Trick 1: ♡10, ♡3, ♡J, ?. Plan the play.

Rubber bridge
Neither vulnerable

North
- ♠ A K 5 3 2
- ♡ A K 8 7 4
- ◇ 3 2
- ♣ 8

South
- ♠ 8 7 6
- ♡ 5 3
- ◇ A K
- ♣ K Q J 10 9 7

W	N	E	S
2◇ [1]	3◇	pass	4NT
pass	5♡	pass	6NT
all pass			
	1. Weak.		

West leads the ◇J. Plan the play.

Rubber bridge
Both vulnerable

North
- ♠ Q J 9
- ♡ K 9 7 3 2
- ◇ K 4
- ♣ 7 6 4

South
- ♠ A 5 4 2
- ♡ J 8
- ◇ A 8
- ♣ K Q J 10 9

W	N	E	S
			1♣
pass	1♡	pass	1♠
pass	2♠	pass	2NT
pass	3NT	all pass	

West leads the ◇2. Plan the play.

PROBLEM 27

Rubber bridge
Both vulnerable

North
♠ A 4 3
♡ 9 4 3 2
◇ 8 6
♣ A K 8 4

South
♠ K J 10 9 8 5
♡ A K Q 5
◇ K 7
♣ 3

W	N	E	S
		3◇	4♠
pass	5♠	pass	6♠
all pass			

Trick 1: ◇5, ◇6, ◇A, ◇7. Trick 2: ◇10, ◇K, ◇3, ◇8. Plan the play.

PROBLEM 28

Rubber bridge
Both vulnerable

North
♠ A K 6
♡ A K 3
◇ 9 3
♣ A 7 5 3 2

South
♠ —
♡ Q J 7 6 2
◇ A K Q J 2
♣ 8 6 4

W	N	E	S
	1♣	pass	1♡
pass	2NT	pass	3◇
pass	4♡	pass	4♠
pass	5♣	pass	7♡
all pass			

Trick 1: ♡10, ♡A, ♡4, ♡2. Trick 2: ♡K, ♡5, ♡6, ♡9. Plan the play.

Rubber bridge
Neither vulnerable

North
♠ 8 7 3 2
♡ Q 10 6
♢ A K
♣ J 9 5 4

South
♠ A Q
♡ K J 9 8 4 3
♢ Q 7 2
♣ A K

W	N	E	S
		1♠	dbl
pass	3♣	pass	3♡
pass	4♡	pass	4♠
pass	5♢	pass	6♡
all pass			

Trick 1: ♠4, ♠2, ♠K, ?. Plan the play.

Rubber bridge
North-South vulnerable

North
♠ A 10 8 5 3
♡ K 7 4
♢ Q J
♣ 9 6 2

South
♠ K
♡ A Q J 6 3
♢ A K
♣ A K 7 5 4

W	N	E	S
			2♣
pass	2♠	pass	3♡
pass	4♡	pass	5♣
pass	5♡	pass	6♡
all pass			

West leads the ♢10. Plan the play.

PROBLEM 31

Rubber bridge
Both vulnerable

North
- ♠ K Q 4 3
- ♡ K Q J
- ◇ 9 8
- ♣ Q J 9 4

South
- ♠ A 10 9 8 6
- ♡ 6
- ◇ J 7 4 2
- ♣ A 6 3

W	N	E	S
1◇	dbl	pass	2♠
3◇	3♠	pass	4♠
all pass			

Trick 1: ◇K, ◇8, ◇5, ◇2. Trick 2: ◇Q, ◇9, ♣2, ◇4. Trick 3: ◇10, ?.
Plan the play.

PROBLEM 32

Rubber bridge
East-West vulnerable

North
- ♠ A Q J 3
- ♡ A 5
- ◇ A K 7 2
- ♣ Q J 5

South
- ♠ K 9
- ♡ Q 7 4
- ◇ 8 6 5
- ♣ A K 10 9 6

W	N	E	S
			1♣
pass	1◇	pass	1NT
pass	2♠	pass	3◇
pass	4♣	pass	5♣
pass	5♡	pass	5♠
pass	7♣	all pass	

West leads the ♣2. Plan the play.

Rubber bridge
East-West vulnerable

North
♠ 7 5 3
♡ 7 6 4
◇ J 10 9
♣ Q J 10 9

South
♠ A K Q 10 8 2
♡ A K Q 3
◇ 3 2
♣ 2

W	N	E	S
			2♣
pass	2◇	pass	2♠
pass	2NT	pass	3♡
pass	3♠	pass	4♠
all pass			

Trick 1: ◇K, ◇ 9, ◇4, ◇2. Trick 2: ◇Q, ◇10, ◇5, ◇3.
Trick 3: ◇A, ◇J, ◇6, ?. Plan the play.

Matchpoints
East-West vulnerable

North
♠ A 9 8 3
♡ Q 6 2
◇ 5 4
♣ K J 10 7

South
♠ 7
♡ K J 10 9 7
◇ Q 8 6
♣ A Q 5 3

W	N	E	S
		pass	1♡
pass	1NT	pass	2♣
pass	3♡	all pass	

Trick 1: ♡4, ♡2, ♡A, ♡7. Trick2: ♡5, ♡9, ♡3, ?.
Plan the play.

PROBLEM 35

Rubber bridge
East-West vulnerable

North
- ♠ A 6 2
- ♡ J 9 8 7
- ♢ J 10 8
- ♣ 7 6 3

South
- ♠ 10 7 5 4 3
- ♡ —
- ♢ A K
- ♣ A K Q 8 5 2

W	N	E	S
			1♣
pass	1♡	pass	2♠
pass	3♣	pass	3♠
pass	4♠	all pass	

West leads the ♡K. (a) Plan the play. (b) Plan the play in 5♣.

PROBLEM 36

Rubber bridge
East-West vulnerable

North
- ♠ A 8 6 5 2
- ♡ A 5 4
- ♢ 6 3 2
- ♣ Q 7

South
- ♠ K 4
- ♡ Q 3
- ♢ A K Q J 10 9 5
- ♣ A K

W	N	E	S
			2♣
pass	2♠	pass	3♢
pass	4♢	pass	5♣
pass	5♡	pass	5♠
pass	7♢	all pass	

West leads the ♢7. Plan the play if East (a) follows (b) discards a club.

Rubber bridge
Both vulnerable

North
♠ A 3 2
♡ 9 5 4
◇ Q J 10
♣ 8 7 6 4

South
♠ K 7
♡ A J 10 8
◇ A K 6
♣ A K Q J

W	N	E	S
			2♣
pass	2◇	pass	3NT
pass	6NT	all pass	

West leads the ♠J.
Plan the play: (a) if things go as expected; (b) if they do not.

Rubber bridge
Both vulnerable

North
♠ A K 2
♡ 9 5 4
◇ J 10 6
♣ 8 7 6 4

South
♠ 7 3
♡ A J 10 8
◇ A K Q
♣ A K Q J

W	N	E	S
			2♣
pass	2◇	pass	2NT
pass	4NT	pass	6NT
all pass			

West leads the ♠J.
Plan the play: (a) if things go as expected; (b) if they do not.

PROBLEM 39

Rubber bridge
East-West vulnerable

North
- ♠ A
- ♡ A 10 8 6 3
- ◇ A Q 4 3
- ♣ Q J 6

South
- ♠ Q 7 3
- ♡ 7
- ◇ K 10 9 5 2
- ♣ A K 10 9

W	N	E	S
	1♡	pass	2◇
pass	3♠	pass	4NT
pass	5♣	pass	5♡
pass	5NT	pass	7◇
all pass			

Trick 1: ♣8, ♣6, ♣2, ♣9. Trick 2: ◇2, ♠2, ◇A, ◇6. Plan the play.

PROBLEM 40

Matchpoints
North-South vulnerable

North
- ♠ A K 8
- ♡ K 10 7 6
- ◇ Q J 9 3 2
- ♣ 2

South
- ♠ Q J 10 6 5 4 3
- ♡ A 3
- ◇ —
- ♣ Q 6 5 3

W	N	E	S
		1NT	pass
2◇¹	pass	2♡	2♠
pass	4♠	all pass	
	1. Transfer.		

Trick 1: ♣J, ♣2, ♣A, ♣3. Trick 2: ♠2, ?. Plan the play.

PROBLEM 41

Rubber bridge
North-South vulnerable

North
- ♠ 10 6 4 2
- ♡ 3
- ◇ A K Q J 9
- ♣ 8 7 5

South
- ♠ A K 9 3
- ♡ A 7 6 4
- ◇ 5 3 2
- ♣ A K

W	N	E	S
			1NT
pass	2♣	pass	2♠
pass	4♡	pass	6♠
all pass			

West leads the ♡Q. (a) Plan the play. (b) Plan the play at matchpoints.

PROBLEM 42

Rubber bridge
Neither vulnerable

North
- ♠ 6 5 3
- ♡ A K J 4
- ◇ J 7 5 2
- ♣ K 10

South
- ♠ A K J
- ♡ Q 7 3 2
- ◇ A K 3
- ♣ A Q J

W	N	E	S
			2♣
pass	2◇	pass	2NT
pass	6NT	all pass	

West leads the ♡10. Plan the play.

PROBLEM 43

Rubber bridge
Both vulnerable

North
- ♠ K Q
- ♡ Q 8 7 4 2
- ◇ Q 6 4
- ♣ 8 4 3

South
- ♠ A 8
- ♡ A K 10 6 3
- ◇ A J 2
- ♣ A K J

W	N	E	S
			2♣
pass	2◇	pass	2NT
pass	3◇	pass	4♡
pass	5♡	pass	6♡
all pass			

West leads the ♠10. Plan the play.

PROBLEM 44

Matchpoints
North-South vulnerable

North
- ♠ 9 7 3
- ♡ K 6 3 2
- ◇ A 10
- ♣ A K Q 10

South
- ♠ K Q
- ♡ A 7 4
- ◇ K Q 4 2
- ♣ J 7 6 3

W	N	E	S
			1♣
2♠	dbl	pass	2NT
pass	6♣	all pass	

Trick 1: ♠A, ♠3, ♠2, ♠Q. Trick 2: ♠J, ♠7, ♠4, ♠K. Plan the play.

PROBLEM 45

Rubber bridge
North-South vulnerable

North
- ♠ J 6 4
- ♡ A 3 2
- ◇ Q 10 7 6 5
- ♣ K 6

South
- ♠ A Q 8 7 3 2
- ♡ 6
- ◇ J 3
- ♣ A 8 3 2

W	N	E	S
		1◇	1♠
3♡[1]	3♠	4♡	4♠
all pass			
	1. Weak.		

Trick 1: ◇4, ◇5, ◇K, ◇J. Trick 2: ◇A, ◇3, ◇2, ◇6. Trick 3: ◇9, ?.
Plan the play.

PROBLEM 46

Rubber bridge
Neither vulnerable

North
- ♠ A Q J 2
- ♡ A K J 2
- ◇ A K Q 2
- ♣ 2

South
- ♠ 10 9 3
- ♡ 10 9 3
- ◇ 9 8
- ♣ A K Q 6 5

W	N	E	S
	2♣	pass	3♣
pass	3◇	pass	3NT
pass	4NT	pass	6NT
all pass			

West leads the ♣J. Plan the play.

PROBLEM 47

Rubber bridge
Both vulnerable

North
- ♠ K 9 8 6 5 4
- ♡ Q 5 3
- ♢ 8 4 2
- ♣ 2

South
- ♠ A 2
- ♡ A 7 6
- ♢ 3
- ♣ A K J 10 7 5 3

W	N	E	S
3♢	pass	pass	5♣
all pass			

Trick 1: ♢K, ♢2, ♢7, ♢3. Trick 2: ♢A, ♢4, ♢Q, ?. Plan the play.

PROBLEM 48

Rubber bridge
Neither vulnerable

North
- ♠ A 10 6 5 2
- ♡ A 6
- ♢ A 2
- ♣ A Q 6 5

South
- ♠ 3
- ♡ K 7 5 2
- ♢ K Q J 5
- ♣ K J 4 3

W	N	E	S
	1♠	pass	2♣
pass	4NT	pass	5♢
pass	5NT	pass	7♣
all pass			

West leads the ♡J. Plan the play.

PROBLEM 49

Matchpoints
North-South vulnerable

North
♠ 4 3 2
♡ 7 6 5 2
◇ 9 4 3
♣ J 7 4

South
♠ A K J 6
♡ A K 8
◇ A 10
♣ 10 9 6 2

W	N	E	S
			1♣
all pass			

Trick 1: ♣A, ♣4, ♣3, ♣2. Trick 2: ♣K, ♣7, ♣5, ♣6.
Trick 3: ◇Q, ◇3, ◇8, ◇10. Trick 4: ◇J, ◇4, ◇7, ◇A.
Trick 5: ♠A, ♠5, ♠2, ♠9. Trick 6: ♠K, ♠7, ♠3, ♠Q.
Plan the play.

PROBLEM 50

Rubber bridge
East-West vulnerable

North
♠ A 5 4
♡ A K Q
◇ K Q 6 4
♣ 7 3 2

South
♠ K 8 6
♡ 10 4 2
◇ A 3
♣ A Q 10 6 4

W	N	E	S
			1♣
pass	1◇	pass	1NT
pass	6NT	all pass	

West leads the ♠J. (a) Plan the play. (b) Plan the play in 7NT.

PROBLEM 51

Rubber bridge
Both vulnerable

North
- ♠ Q 6 4
- ♡ J 9 4 3
- ◇ 8 6 5
- ♣ A J 4

South
- ♠ A K
- ♡ 10 6 5
- ◇ A K 2
- ♣ K 7 6 5 3

W	N	E	S
		2♠	2NT
pass	3NT	all pass	

West leads the ♠5. Plan the play.

PROBLEM 52

Rubber bridge
East-West vulnerable

North
- ♠ A 8 6 2
- ♡ 7 6 2
- ◇ A 5 4 3
- ♣ K Q

South
- ♠ 9
- ♡ A K Q 5 4 3
- ◇ K 8 2
- ♣ A J 5

W	N	E	S
			1♡
pass	1♠	pass	3♡
pass	6♡	all pass	

Trick 1: ♡J, ♡2, ♣2, ?.
(a) Plan the play. (b) A leading writer says that West must have a specific shape for South to succeed. Must he?

Rubber bridge
Neither vulnerable

North
♠ 5 3
♡ A Q 2
♢ A K 8 7 6 3
♣ K 6

South
♠ A K 10 7 6
♡ K J 10 4 3
♢ 5 4
♣ 5

W	N	E	S
	1♢	1♠	pass
pass	dbl	pass	pass
2♣	2♢	pass	3♡
pass	4♣	pass	4♠
pass	6♡	all pass	

West leads the ♠2. Plan the play.

Rubber bridge
Both vulnerable

North
♠ 9 6 5
♡ K 10 4
♢ 8 7 3 2
♣ A Q J

South
♠ A
♡ A 5 2
♢ A Q J
♣ K 10 9 8 7 5

W	N	E	S
			1♣
2♣¹	3♣	pass	6♣
all pass			
	1. Majors.		

Trick 1: ♠K, ♠5, ♠2, ♠A. Trick 2: ♣7, ♣4, ♣J, ♣2.
Trick 3: ♠6, ♠3, ♣8, ♠7. Trick 4: ♣9, ♣6, ♣A, ♣3. Plan the play.

PROBLEM 55

Rubber bridge
Both vulnerable

North
- ♠ 5 3
- ♡ A 7 4
- ◊ J 9 7 4 2
- ♣ Q 8 5

South
- ♠ A K 7 4 2
- ♡ 8 5
- ◊ A K Q
- ♣ K J 7

W	N	E	S
		3♣	dbl
pass	3◊	pass	3NT
all pass			

Trick 1: ♡K, ♡4, ♡2, ♡5. Trick 2: ♡Q, ♡7, ♡6, ♡8.
Trick 3: ♡J, ♡A, ♡10, ?. Plan the play.

PROBLEM 56

Matchpoints
East-West vulnerable

North
- ♠ K 10 8 3
- ♡ 7 5
- ◊ Q J
- ♣ A 9 6 4 2

South
- ♠ J 4
- ♡ A 10 6
- ◊ A K 8 6 4
- ♣ K Q J

W	N	E	S
			1NT
pass	2♣	pass	2◊
pass	3NT	all pass	

West leads the ♠2. Plan the play.

Rubber bridge
East-West vulnerable

North
♠ Q 8 4 3
♡ 8 5 4 3
◊ 7 5
♣ K 5 3

South
♠ J 9
♡ A K Q J 10 7
◊ A Q 10
♣ Q 2

W	N	E	S
			1♡
1♠	2♡	pass	4♡
all pass			

Trick 1: ♠K, ♠3, ♠10, ♠9. Trick 2: ♠A, ♠4, ♠2, ♠J.
Trick 3: ♠6, ♠8, ♡6, ?. Plan the play.

Rubber bridge
Both vulnerable

North
♠ Q 8 4 3
♡ 10 8 5 4
◊ 7 5
♣ K 5 3

South
♠ J 9
♡ A K Q J 7 3
◊ A Q 10
♣ Q 2

W	N	E	S
			1♡
pass	2♡	pass	4♡
all pass			

Trick 1: ♠5, ♠3, ♠A, ♠9. Trick 2: ♠10, ♠J, ♠K, ♠4.
Trick 3: ♠6, ♠8, ♡6, ?. Plan the play.

PROBLEM 59

Rubber bridge
North-South vulnerable

North
- ♠ Q J 10 9
- ♡ A 7 6 4 3
- ◇ 8
- ♣ 7 5 2

South
- ♠ K 8 7 5 3
- ♡ 10
- ◇ A K 4 3 2
- ♣ A K

W	N	E	S
			1♠
3♣[1]	4♠	pass	4NT
pass	5◇	pass	6♠
all pass			
	1. Preemptive.		

Trick 1: ♠A, ♠9, ♠4, ♠3. Trick 2: ♠2, ♠10, ♠6, ?. Plan the play.

PROBLEM 60

Rubber bridge
North-South vulnerable

North
- ♠ Q J 10 9
- ♡ A 7 6 3
- ◇ 8 5
- ♣ A 5 2

South
- ♠ K 8 7 5 3
- ♡ 10
- ◇ A K 4 3 2
- ♣ K 7

W	N	E	S
		3♣	3♠
pass	4♣	pass	4◇
pass	6♠	all pass	

Trick 1: ♠A, ♠9, ♠4, ♠3. Trick 2: ♠2, ♠10, ♠6, ?. Plan the play.

PROBLEM 61

Rubber bridge
Neither vulnerable

North
- ♠ 9 8
- ♡ Q J 10
- ◇ A K 5 3 2
- ♣ 7 6 4

South
- ♠ Q J 7
- ♡ A K
- ◇ J 10 9 6
- ♣ K Q J 8

W	N	E	S
			1NT
pass	3NT	all pass	

Trick 1: ♠5 (4th best), ♠8, ♠A, ♠7. Trick 2: ♠4, ♠Q, ♠2, ♠9.
Plan the play.

PROBLEM 62

Rubber bridge
Neither vulnerable

North
- ♠ Q 9 4 3
- ♡ K 7
- ◇ J 10 6 5
- ♣ A 8 2

South
- ♠ A K 8 7 5
- ♡ 10
- ◇ Q 3 2
- ♣ J 9 6 4

W	N	E	S
		1♡	1♠
pass	2♡	dbl	pass
pass	2♠	3♡	3♠
all pass			

Trick 1: ♡2, ♡7, ♡Q, ♡10. Trick 2: ◇K, ◇2, ◇7, ◇5.
Trick 3: ◇A, ◇Q, ◇8, ◇6. Trick 4: ♡A, ?. Plan the play.

PROBLEM 63

Rubber bridge
Neither vulnerable

North
- ♠ 10 8 7 5 4 2
- ♡ 6
- ◇ Q 9
- ♣ A 10 9 4

South
- ♠ J
- ♡ K
- ◇ A K J 8 7 3 2
- ♣ K 8 7 5

W	N	E	S
pass	pass	3♡	4◇
4♡	5◇	all pass	

Trick 1: ♠K, ♠2, ♠6, ♠J. Trick 2: ♠3, ♠4, ♠Q, ?. Plan the play.

PROBLEM 64

Rubber bridge
East-West vulnerable

North
- ♠ Q 7 3
- ♡ A K 8 6 5
- ◇ J 4
- ♣ 10 9 2

South
- ♠ A K J 10 6
- ♡ 4 3
- ◇ K Q 10 5 3
- ♣ A

W	N	E	S
			1♠
pass	2♡	pass	3◇
pass	3♠	pass	4◇
pass	4♡	pass	5♣
pass	5♡	pass	6♠
all pass			

Trick 1: ♣K, ♣2, ♣8, ♣A. Trick 2: ♠A, ♠2, ♠3, ♠4.
(a) Plan the play. (b) Plan the play if North's ♡6 is the ♣6.

Rubber bridge
North-South vulnerable

North
- ♠ K 10 7
- ♡ A K 6
- ◇ A 6 4 3 2
- ♣ K 5

South
- ♠ A Q 6 2
- ♡ J 5 2
- ◇ —
- ♣ A Q J 10 8 6

W	N	E	S
			1♣
pass	1◇	pass	1♠
pass	2♡	pass	4♣
pass	4NT	pass	5♠
pass	7♣	all pass	

West leads the ◇Q. Plan the play.

Rubber bridge
North-South vulnerable

North
- ♠ 6 4 2
- ♡ K J 10 6 2
- ◇ 9 7 4
- ♣ K J

South
- ♠ A Q J
- ♡ A 4
- ◇ Q J 10 8 6 5
- ♣ A Q

W	N	E	S
			1◇
pass	1♡	pass	3NT
all pass			

West leads the ♣5. Plan the play.

PROBLEM 67

Rubber bridge
North-South vulnerable

North
- ♠ A J 5 4 3
- ♡ K 7
- ◇ 10 8
- ♣ Q 9 6 2

South
- ♠ Q
- ♡ A 9 6 5 4 3 2
- ◇ A 5
- ♣ K J 10

W	N	E	S
			1♡
pass	1♠	pass	2♡
pass	3♡	pass	4♡
all pass			

West leads the ◇3. Plan the play.

PROBLEM 68

Rubber bridge
Both vulnerable

North
- ♠ 10 8 6
- ♡ 7 5 4
- ◇ 9 8 6
- ♣ K Q J 7

South
- ♠ A K Q 7 5 2
- ♡ A K 6 2
- ◇ A K 3
- ♣ —

W	N	E	S
			2♣
pass	2◇	pass	2♠
pass	2NT	pass	3♡
pass	3♠	pass	4◇
pass	4♠	pass	5♠
all pass			

West leads the ♣A. Plan the play.

Rubber bridge
North-South vulnerable

North
- ♠ 10 9 5
- ♡ K 9 4
- ◇ 4 3
- ♣ A 10 9 5 3

South
- ♠ K 7
- ♡ A 2
- ◇ A K Q 10 6 5
- ♣ K Q 6

W	N	E	S
1♠	pass	pass	3NT
pass	4NT	pass	6NT
all pass			

Trick 1: ♡Q, ♡4, ♡6, ♡A. Trick 2: ◇A, ♠6, ◇3, ◇2. Plan the play.

Rubber bridge
Both vulnerable

North
- ♠ A 10
- ♡ 9 7 4 2
- ◇ K J 6 5
- ♣ 10 8 7

South
- ♠ K Q J
- ♡ A K
- ◇ Q 9 4 2
- ♣ A K Q 5

W	N	E	S
			2♣
pass	2◇	pass	2NT
pass	4NT	pass	6NT
all pass			

Trick 1: ♡Q, ♡2, ♡3, ♡A. Trick 2: ◇2, ◇3, ◇J, ◇8. Plan the play.

PROBLEM 71

Matchpoints
North-South vulnerable

North
- ♠ A 4
- ♡ 10 7
- ◇ A J 10 9 6 4
- ♣ A K 3

South
- ♠ K Q 7
- ♡ A 8 4 3
- ◇ Q 7
- ♣ Q J 7 5

W	N	E	S
			1♣
pass	1◇	pass	1NT
pass	6NT	all pass	

West leads the ♡K. Plan the play.

PROBLEM 72

Rubber bridge
Both vulnerable

North
- ♠ J 5 4 2
- ♡ Q 10 7
- ◇ 6
- ♣ A K 9 8 3

South
- ♠ A Q 8 6 3
- ♡ 4 3
- ◇ A K Q 8 7
- ♣ 4

W	N	E	S
		2♡	2♠
pass	4♠	all pass	

Trick 1: ♡9, ♡10, ♡J, ♡4. Trick 2: ♡A, ♡3, ♡5, ♡7. Trick 3: ♡K, ?.
Plan the play.

PROBLEM 73

Rubber bridge
Neither vulnerable

North
- ♠ Q 7 4 3
- ♡ J 8 6 2
- ◇ A 5
- ♣ K 10 9

South
- ♠ K 5
- ♡ A Q 4
- ◇ K Q 9 8 3
- ♣ A 6 2

W	N	E	S
			1◇
pass	1♡	pass	2NT
pass	3NT	all pass	

West leads the ♠J. Plan the play.

PROBLEM 74

Rubber bridge
Both vulnerable

North
- ♠ J 9 3
- ♡ 10 5 3 2
- ◇ K Q 5 4 2
- ♣ 4

South
- ♠ K Q 4 2
- ♡ A K
- ◇ A 6 3
- ♣ Q J 9 6

W	N	E	S
			1♣
1♠	dbl	pass	2NT
pass	3NT	all pass	

Trick 1: ♠7, ♠9, ♠5, ?. Plan the play.

PROBLEM 75

Rubber bridge
North-South vulnerable

North
♠ K J 3
♡ A K J
♢ A K 7 2
♣ A J 3

South
♠ A 10 4
♡ Q 8 7
♢ J 3
♣ K 9 6 5 2

W	N	E	S
	2♣	pass	2NT
pass	3NT	pass	6NT
all pass			

West leads the ♠2. Plan the play.

PROBLEM 76

Rubber bridge
North-South vulnerable

North
♠ K J 10
♡ 8 7 6 2
♢ A
♣ Q 9 5 4 2

South
♠ A Q 9 7 5 2
♡ —
♢ K 8 5
♣ K J 6 3

W	N	E	S
			1♠
4♡	4♠	5♡	6♠
all pass			

West leads the ♡4. Plan the play.

Rubber bridge
East-West vulnerable

North
♠ A J 9 8 7 6
♡ Q J
◊ A J 9
♣ A 2

South
♠ K 5 4
♡ A K
◊ K 10
♣ K Q J 6 5 3

W	N	E	S
			1♣
pass	1♠	pass	2NT
pass	7NT	all pass	

West leads the ♣10. Plan the play.

Rubber bridge
Both vulnerable

North
♠ K 10 7 6
♡ A 6 5
◊ 7 2
♣ A 6 4 3

South
♠ A 4
♡ K Q 10 4 2
◊ K J 10 3
♣ Q 5

W	N	E	S
			1♡
2◊	3♡	pass	4♡
all pass			

West leads the ♠2 (lowest from an odd number of cards).
Plan the play.

PROBLEM 79

Rubber bridge
North-South vulnerable

North
- ♠ A J 6 3
- ♡ K 5 4
- ◇ Q 9 2
- ♣ 10 8 7

South
- ♠ 9 7 4
- ♡ A Q J 10 9 8
- ◇ J
- ♣ A K 3

W	N	E	S
		1♠	2♡
pass	2♠	pass	4♡
all pass			

West leads the ♠2. Plan the play.

PROBLEM 80

Rubber bridge
East-West vulnerable

North
- ♠ J 8 7 2
- ♡ Q 4
- ◇ A Q 9 6
- ♣ 8 4 3

South
- ♠ 3
- ♡ A K
- ◇ K J 10
- ♣ K Q 9 7 6 5 2

W	N	E	S
			1♣
pass	1♠	pass	3♣
pass	4♣	pass	5♣
all pass			

West leads the ♡10. Plan the play.

PROBLEM 81

Rubber bridge
North-South vulnerable

North
- ♠ K J 9 8 3 2
- ♡ A
- ◇ Q 10 7
- ♣ 7 6 5

South
- ♠ —
- ♡ K 6 4 2
- ◇ A K J 9 8 5
- ♣ A Q 3

W	N	E	S
			1◇
pass	1♠	pass	2♡
pass	2♠	pass	3◇
pass	5◇	pass	6◇
all pass			

West leads the ◇2. Plan the play.

PROBLEM 82

Rubber bridge
East-West vulnerable

North
- ♠ Q J 4 2
- ♡ K 6 4
- ◇ 10 9 4 3
- ♣ Q 3

South
- ♠ A 10 9 7 6 3
- ♡ A 2
- ◇ A Q
- ♣ 10 6 4

W	N	E	S
			1♠
2♣	2♠	pass	4♠
all pass			

Trick 1: ♣K, ♣3, ♣8, ♣4. Trick 2: ♡J, ?. Plan the play.

PROBLEM 83

Rubber bridge
East-West vulnerable

North
- ♠ Q 3
- ♡ A Q
- ◇ 9 7 5 4 3 2
- ♣ A K 8

South
- ♠ 10 9 6 5 4 2
- ♡ J 8 3
- ◇ A K
- ♣ Q 7

W	N	E	S
	1◇	pass	1♠
pass	2◇	pass	2♠
pass	3♠	pass	4♠
all pass			

Trick 1: ♡2, ♡Q, ♡K, ♡3. Trick 2: ♡7, ?. Plan the play.

PROBLEM 84

Rubber bridge
Neither vulnerable

North
- ♠ K 7 6
- ♡ 7 6 5 3
- ◇ J
- ♣ A K Q 8 4

South
- ♠ Q 10 4 2
- ♡ A K Q J 10 8
- ◇ A
- ♣ 9 3

W	N	E	S
			1♡
pass	4◇	pass	6♡
all pass			

Trick 1: ♡2, ♡5, ♡9, ?. Plan the play.

Rubber bridge
Both vulnerable

North
- ♠ Q 7
- ♡ K 9 6
- ◇ J 10 8 7 4
- ♣ J 7 5

South
- ♠ A 10 8
- ♡ 10 8 4
- ◇ A Q 5
- ♣ A K Q 2

W	N	E	S
			1♣
dbl	1◇	pass	2NT
pass	3NT	all pass	

West leads the ♡3. Plan the play.

Rubber bridge
Both vulnerable

North
- ♠ 8 4
- ♡ K 10 6
- ◇ J 3
- ♣ A Q 9 7 5 2

South
- ♠ K 10 9
- ♡ A Q J
- ◇ A K Q 9 6
- ♣ K 10

W	N	E	S
			2♣
pass	3♣	pass	3NT
pass	6NT	all pass	

West leads the ♡9. Plan the play.

PROBLEM 87

Rubber bridge
Neither vulnerable

North
- ♠ A Q 6
- ♡ K 8
- ◇ J 10 9
- ♣ 7 5 4 3 2

South
- ♠ K 8 5 4
- ♡ A 3
- ◇ K Q 6
- ♣ A 9 8 6

W	N	E	S
			1NT
pass	3NT	all pass	

West leads the ♡J. Plan the play.

PROBLEM 88

Rubber bridge
Neither vulnerable

North
- ♠ 9 6 5
- ♡ A J
- ◇ K Q 10 8
- ♣ 10 9 8 3

South
- ♠ K Q J 10 3 2
- ♡ Q 5
- ◇ A 5
- ♣ A Q 6

W	N	E	S
			1♠
pass	1NT	pass	3NT
pass	4♠	pass	6♠
all pass			

West leads the ♡4. Plan the play.

PROBLEM 89

Rubber bridge
Neither vulnerable

North
♠ 7 4 3
♡ A 10 9 7 6 4 2
♢ —
♣ A Q J

South
♠ A 9 6
♡ K 3
♢ A K 2
♣ K 10 9 8 7

W	N	E	S
3♢	3♡	pass	4♣
pass	6♣	pass	7♣
all pass			

West leads the ♢Q. Plan the play.

PROBLEM 90

Rubber bridge
Both vulnerable

North
♠ 6 2
♡ 8 7 5 3
♢ A J 10 9 4
♣ 10 2

South
♠ J 10 5 4
♡ A Q J
♢ K 6
♣ A K J 9

W	N	E	S
pass	pass	1♣	dbl
pass	1♡	pass	2NT
pass	3NT	all pass	

West leads the ♣8. Plan the play.

PROBLEM 91

Rubber bridge
East-West vulnerable

North
- ♠ J 7
- ♡ 3
- ♢ K 5 4 3
- ♣ A K Q 7 6 4

South
- ♠ A K
- ♡ Q 10 9 6 4 2
- ♢ A J 10 2
- ♣ 5

W	N	E	S
			1♡
pass	2♣	pass	2♢
pass	3♢	pass	3♡
pass	4♣	pass	4♠
pass	5♢	all pass	

West leads the ♠4. Plan the play.

PROBLEM 92

Rubber bridge
Both vulnerable

North
- ♠ A Q 10
- ♡ A Q J 10 6
- ♢ A 9 3
- ♣ A K

South
- ♠ 9 8 7
- ♡ K 5
- ♢ K J 8 7 2
- ♣ J 10 4

W	N	E	S
pass	2♣	pass	2NT
pass	3♡	pass	3NT
pass	6NT	all pass	

West leads the ♡9. Plan the play.

PROBLEM 93

Rubber bridge
Neither vulnerable

North
♠ 5 4 3
♡ K J 7 2
◇ 6 2
♣ A K 9 2

South
♠ A Q 10 8 7
♡ A 3
◇ Q J 10 7
♣ 6 5

W	N	E	S
			1♠
pass	1NT	pass	2◇
pass	3♠	pass	4♠
all pass			

Trick 1: ◇K, ◇2, ◇5, ◇7. Trick 2: ◇A, ◇6, ◇4, ◇10. Trick 3: ◇8, ?.
Plan the play.

PROBLEM 94

Rubber bridge
East-West vulnerable

North
♠ A K Q J 5
♡ Q 9 8 2
◇ Q 7
♣ A K

South
♠ 10 8 4 3 2
♡ A K 7 4
◇ A
♣ 8 7 4

W	N	E	S
			1♠
pass	4NT	pass	5♡
pass	7♠	all pass	

Trick 1: ♣J, ♣A, ♣2, ♣4. Trick 2: ♠A, ♠6, ♠2, ◇2.
Plan the play.

PROBLEM 95

Rubber bridge
North-South vulnerable

North
- ♠ J 10 5
- ♡ 8 7 3
- ◇ K 9 2
- ♣ K Q 6 4

South
- ♠ A K Q 6 4 3 2
- ♡ A 6 2
- ◇ 4
- ♣ A 3

W	N	E	S
			2♣
pass	2NT	3NT	4♠
5♣	dbl	5◇	pass
pass	5♠	pass	6♠
all pass			

West leads the ♡9. Plan the play.

PROBLEM 96

Rubber bridge
North-South vulnerable

North
- ♠ A K
- ♡ K Q 7 6 4
- ◇ J 6 5 2
- ♣ 8 6

South
- ♠ 8 7 6 5
- ♡ A 2
- ◇ A Q 7 4 3
- ♣ A 2

W	N	E	S
pass	1♡	pass	2◇
pass	3◇	pass	4♣
pass	4♠	pass	6◇
all pass			

West leads the ♣Q. Plan the play.

PROBLEM 97

Rubber bridge
Neither vulnerable

North
♠ A K J 5 4
♡ A Q 9 4
♢ —
♣ A J 10 7

South
♠ Q 10 8 7 3
♡ J 2
♢ A
♣ K 9 6 5 4

W	N	E	S
3♢	dbl	4♢	4♠
pass	6♠	all pass	

West leads the ♢Q. Plan the play.

PROBLEM 98

Rubber bridge
Both vulnerable

North
♠ A Q 10 9
♡ 8
♢ Q 7 5 4
♣ K 10 9 4

South
♠ 7
♡ 4 3
♢ K J 10 9 8 6
♣ A Q 5 2

W	N	E	S
			1♢
2♢[1]	3♢[2]	4♡	5♢
all pass			
	1. Majors.		
	2. Splinter.		

West leads the ♣3. Plan the play.

PROBLEM 99

Rubber bridge
East-West vulnerable

North
- ♠ A Q 6 5 2
- ♡ K 10 4 3
- ◇ A Q
- ♣ 8 7

South
- ♠ K 10
- ♡ A Q 8 5 2
- ◇ K 9
- ♣ A 6 4 3

W	N	E	S
			1♡
pass	2♠	pass	2NT
pass	3♡	pass	4NT
pass	5♣	pass	5NT
pass	6♡	all pass	

West leads the ♣J. Plan the play.

PROBLEM 100

Rubber bridge
East-West vulnerable

North
- ♠ A K 5 4
- ♡ 5 3 2
- ◇ Q J
- ♣ A K J 10

South
- ♠ 3 2
- ♡ A K Q J 10 4
- ◇ —
- ♣ 9 8 7 6 5

W	N	E	S
			1♡
pass	1♠	pass	2♡
pass	3♣	pass	4◇
pass	6♡	all pass	

Trick 1: ◇4, ◇J, ◇K, ♡10. Trick 2: ♡A, ♡6, ♡2, ◇5. Plan the play.

North
- ♠ 5 4
- ♡ K Q 10
- ◊ K 5 2
- ♣ A K 8 5 4

West
- ♠ A K Q J
- ♡ 8 5 4 3 2
- ◊ —
- ♣ 10 9 7 6

East
- ♠ 10 9 8 6
- ♡ 9 6
- ◊ J 10 7 3
- ♣ Q J 2

South
- ♠ 7 3 2
- ♡ A J 7
- ◊ A Q 9 8 6 4
- ♣ 3

5◊ by South
Lead: ♠K

Declarer must ruff twice in his hand to reduce to trump parity with East, then wind up in dummy with a major tenace in trumps in the South hand. The entries to do this are available: you can lead a trump now to create the major tenace in diamonds; one club and two hearts can be used for the two ruffs and late re-entry. The play should go: diamond to the ten and queen; club king; club ruff; heart to dummy; club ruff; heart to dummy. If all this succeeds, declarer is home. He plays a winning club from dummy, intending to discard the ace of hearts, and end in a coup position if East does not ruff.

There are some trump reduction situations in which winners must be cashed early to avoid their being ruffed later, stranding declarer with losers in his long trump hand. This is the reverse situation. Cashing dummy's second club winner early is unnecessary (because declarer will end up with a side-suit winner in the ace of hearts) and fails in the distribution shown in the diagram because East discards his second heart on the fourth round of clubs. To see the difference, replay the contract with ace-king-third of hearts in dummy opposite three small in declarer's hand.

SOLUTION 2

North
- ♠ 4 2
- ♡ A K 5
- ◇ J 9 7
- ♣ J 7 6 3 2

West
- ♠ J 10 8 7
- ♡ J 9 7 2
- ◇ 10 6
- ♣ K 10 9

East
- ♠ 6 5 3
- ♡ 8 6 4 3
- ◇ 8 5 3 2
- ♣ Q 8

South
- ♠ A K Q 9
- ♡ Q 10
- ◇ A K Q 4
- ♣ A 5 4

6NT by South
Lead: ♠J

This solution may raise more questions than it settles, but some situations are like that. With problems existing in only the black suits, things seem simple enough, but... First of all, declarer must choose between two basic approaches: an endplay against West, and a black-suit squeeze. This in itself is a difficult decision.

We like the squeeze possibility because it will (usually) lead to success when West has led from jack-ten-third of spades; to us, jack-ten-fourth is a less comfortable lead against the given auction. Assuming declarer prefers to look for the squeeze, what declarer would like to do is lose a club trick early; later on he will cash the ace of clubs, run diamonds, and then cash the hearts (to end in dummy); finally, if the jack of clubs is not high, try to run spades. This will succeed if declarer is lucky in spades, and finds the ten dropping early, or if he is very lucky in clubs, or if he squeezes West in the black suits. For the squeeze to work, West must be long in clubs and the club trick must be lost to West, because if East gets the lead in clubs he can return a spade to destroy the squeeze position.

Assuming West has, say, three clubs, what is the best way to lose a club trick to West? Low towards dummy works against East's holding ten-nine, ten-eight or nine-eight. Low from dummy works against East's holding king-eight, queen-eight, nine-eight, and also against a sleepy East holding ten-eight. Low from dummy also allows South to preserve the chance that East was dealt singleton king or queen. However, there are some little traps along the way. Suppose East plays an honor on the lead from dummy. In theory, declarer should win the ace and lead to dummy's jack, to preserve all his chances. However, East might fool declarer by playing an honor from king-queen-ten or the like, inducing declarer to go down by playing on clubs when the spades were dropping all along. What is declarer supposed to do about that? We don't rightly know. But we suspect that the best way to start the play is to win the spade, play a diamond to the jack (you need to use dummy's heart entry last to work the squeeze), play a low club, and cross any further bridges when you come to them.

SOLUTION 3

North
♠ A K
♡ A Q J 10
◇ Q J 10 9
♣ 9 5 4

West
♠ Q J 9 8 6
♡ K 7 4 2
◇ K 2
♣ 3 2

East
♠ 10 7 5 4 3 2
♡ 6 5 3
◇ 8 7 6 5
♣ —

South
♠ —
♡ 9 8
◇ A 4 3
♣ A K Q J 10 8 7 6

7♣ by South
Lead: ♠Q

Declarer can maneuver to ruff a card in one red suit or the other, trying to drop a king-doubleton of that suit, then fall back on a finesse in the other red suit. To ruff a heart, declarer wins two spades in dummy, pitching hearts, ruffs a heart high, draws trumps ending in dummy, cashes the ace of hearts, and, if dummy's hearts are not good, finesses in diamonds. To ruff a diamond, declarer pitches a diamond at Trick 1, draws trumps from the South hand, unblocks the ace of diamonds, enters dummy with the club nine, pitches his remaining diamond on dummy's second high spade, and ruffs a diamond. If dummy's diamonds are not good, South falls back on a heart finesse.

Which plan is better? The plan in which declarer ruffs a diamond is more likely to succeed because the king is more likely to drop doubleton in the red suit where the opponents have fewer cards.

SOLUTION 4

North
- ♠ Q 7
- ♡ Q 8 2
- ◊ A J 9 6
- ♣ A K Q 2

West
- ♠ K 10 9
- ♡ A J 9 7 5 4
- ◊ 2
- ♣ 10 6 5

East
- ♠ J 5 4 3 2
- ♡ 10 3
- ◊ 8 7 5 4 3
- ♣ 8

South
- ♠ A 8 6
- ♡ K 6
- ◊ K Q 10
- ♣ J 9 7 4 3

6♣ by South
Lead: ◊ 2

A. Declarer should play on the presumption that West has the heart ace and spade king for his overcall. He should win the opening lead and draw trumps. Assuming trumps are not 4-0, declarer should win the third trump in the South hand, to lead the six of hearts. If West goes up with his ace, it's all over. If the heart queen wins, declarer can finish the diamonds to pitch the king of hearts, and later ruff a spade in dummy. If either opponent is void of trumps, the simplest thing for declarer to do is draw trumps and continue as in part B.

B. In notrump, you have to do a bit more work. Well, that's only fair if you expect to get the top score (at matchpoints, perhaps). After winning the opening lead, declarer should lead his six of hearts at once. West may get panicky (especially at matchpoints) and take his ace immediately, which would end the problem. If West lets the heart queen win in dummy, South should run the minors. Then, if West has kept the king of spades protected, he can be thrown in with his ace of hearts; alternatively, if West blanks the spade king, declarer can drop it. South has to guess West's distribution — that's the extra work.

North
- ♠ 7 6 5
- ♡ 8 6 5
- ◇ 7 6 4
- ♣ A K J 3

West
- ♠ K 10 9
- ♡ 4 2
- ◇ J 8 5 3 2
- ♣ 10 6 2

East
- ♠ 3
- ♡ K 10 9 7 3
- ◇ Q 10 9
- ♣ Q 9 5 4

South
- ♠ A Q J 8 4 2
- ♡ A Q J
- ◇ A K
- ♣ 8 7

6♠ by South
Lead: ♣2

South's problem is how best to use his two club entries to dummy. The simplest and best plan is to take two heart finesses. Declarer wins Trick 1 in dummy, and finesses in hearts. If the finesse wins, he plays ace, queen of spades; later, he uses dummy's remaining club honor to repeat the heart finesse. This approach has several advantages over taking a trump finesse. First, the heart finesse, if successful, will almost certainly land the contract; the spade finesse, if successful, still has to overcome the peril of a singleton club in one hand or the other — West's lead need not be honest. Second, speaking of being honest, it will be very difficult for West to fool declarer by holding up his heart king at Trick 2 (when East has, say, king-doubleton of spades).

West cannot be sure declarer has a second heart finesse available when South leads a heart to his queen. In contrast, West would be fairly safe (considering the bidding) to hold up his spade king, from three to the king, if declarer took a trump finesse. This might mislead declarer into repeating the trump finesse instead of catching the doubleton king of hearts in the East hand. Finally, even if one assumes no deception by West, the extra chance of East's holding the heart king singleton or doubleton is small compared to his chance of holding the short king of spades if declarer does his finessing in hearts.

SOLUTION 6

North
- ♠ 3
- ♡ A K
- ◇ K 10 8 3
- ♣ A K 8 6 4 3

West
- ♠ Q
- ♡ 9 8 6 5 4 3
- ◇ 7 4
- ♣ Q 10 9 2

East
- ♠ A J 10 9 2
- ♡ J 10 7 2
- ◇ 6 5 2
- ♣ J

South
- ♠ K 8 7 6 5 4
- ♡ Q
- ◇ A Q J 9
- ♣ 7 5

6◇ by South
Lead: ♠Q

One possible plan is to try to establish spades: diamond nine, spade ruff, diamond to the jack, spade ruff, heart and a heart ruff, last trump. This will succeed if spades are 3-3 or 4-2 and trumps are splitting well. That plan can be improved upon by cashing (or trying to cash — the opening lead is a bit suspicious, considering the auction) the spade king early. If spades break, declarer learns about it in time to save himself a ruffing entry back to the closed hand; he can survive if trumps are 4-1. A cross-ruff might work, but it depends on getting the king of spades through, and on an even club break (needed to allow declarer to cash all his side-suit winners).

If clubs are going to break (and as long as diamonds are not five-zero), declarer might as well win the trump and play three rounds of clubs, hoping to avoid the risk of playing the king of spades. However, if declarer decides to stake his fortunes on the club suit, he can improve his chances further. The best play is to win the diamond queen, and, if West follows, lead a club to the ace, cash the two top hearts throwing a club, then ruff a club with the diamond ace. If clubs break 3-2, declarer can draw trumps from dummy and claim. If clubs turn out to be 4-1, declarer can continue with the diamond nine to dummy's ten, another club ruff, a spade ruff, and the last trump, succeeding if diamonds break. Essentially, this line allows a make if either minor suit splits 3-2.

North
- ♠ 3
- ♡ K Q 6
- ◇ 8 6 4 3
- ♣ A K 6 5 2

West
- ♠ A K 10 9 6
- ♡ 8 7 5 3
- ◇ Q J 2
- ♣ 4

East
- ♠ J 8 5 4 2
- ♡ 9 2
- ◇ 10 9 5
- ♣ Q J 10

South
- ♠ Q 7
- ♡ A J 10 4
- ◇ A K 7
- ♣ 9 8 7 3

4♡ by South
Lead: ♠K

Extreme splits that might affect declarer's choice of play, such as a 5-1 break in either red suit, are strongly contra-indicated by the line of defense, and by East-West's relative inactivity during the auction. Thus, it is fairly safe for declarer to concentrate on guarding against common distributions. He cannot afford to draw trumps before clubs are cleared, lest a 4-2 heart split leave him without trump control. But he also cannot afford to crash out the ace-king of clubs lest the second honor be ruffed; the defense would have time to expose declarer's diamond loser before clubs are established.

Leading towards the second club honor is an improvement, but the entry position is awkward and, anyway, it may be East who ruffs. Declarer can guard against most situations by planning to lose a club trick early. He should lead a high spot (to start unblocking the suit) and lose the trick. (If West covers, declarer can win and return a low club, again unblocking from the closed hand.) In order for this play to fail, an opponent must have a red-suit singleton, or there must be a 4-0 club break.

SOLUTION 8

North
- ♠ A Q 10
- ♡ J 8 7
- ◊ K 5 3 2
- ♣ A 5 3

West
- ♠ 9 5 4
- ♡ 4 3 2
- ◊ Q 10 6
- ♣ J 10 9 8

East
- ♠ 8 7 3 2
- ♡ Q 10 6 5
- ◊ 7
- ♣ Q 7 4 2

South
- ♠ K J 6
- ♡ A K 9
- ◊ A J 9 8 4
- ♣ K 6

6◊ by South
Lead: ♣J

The main question is whether declarer should take the safety play to avoid losing two trump tricks in the event of a 4-0 trump break. Unfortunately, losing only one trump trick is of limited utility to declarer if he cannot endplay the opponents with that one trump trick, because he will still be an underdog in the heart suit. In contrast, declarer will never be worse than about 50-50 if he can force the opponents to lead hearts. Therefore, South should give up on the possibility that West has queen-ten-seven-six of diamonds in exchange for the chance of picking up trumps with no losers when East has all four.

With that in mind, and in view of the fact that the diamond four is declarer's only possible late entry to dummy if his attempted endplay fails, the play should go: club king; diamond eight to dummy's king (if West shows out, declarer plays to pick up trumps); diamond deuce to the ace (if the queen has fallen, declarer draws trumps); club ace; club ruff with the nine; spades (if it is East who has a trump trick, declarer interposes a lead to his heart ace); if no one ruffs, the diamond three and jack to throw in the defender with the diamond queen. If East wins and leads a heart, declarer has little choice but to play East for the heart queen. However, if it is West who is thrown in, declarer takes his best guess on West's heart exit. If that does not work out well, declarer wins and gets to dummy by leading the four of diamonds to the five, in order to take a heart finesse. This succeeds when East was dealt both heart honors (and in a few other unlikely cases, including defensive error).

SOLUTION 9

North
- ♠ J 10 6
- ♡ J 9 7 5
- ◇ A K 4 2
- ♣ A 5

West
- ♠ A K Q 8 4
- ♡ Q 10 6 3
- ◇ J
- ♣ 10 9 8

East
- ♠ 9 7 2
- ♡ 8
- ◇ 10 9 8 6 5 3
- ♣ 7 4 3

South
- ♠ 5 3
- ♡ A K 4 2
- ◇ Q 7
- ♣ K Q J 6 2

4♡ by South
Lead: ♠K

Declarer must plan to run clubs without leading any more trumps, so there is no chance if West has a void or singleton in clubs. Even if West holds two or more clubs, declarer cannot guarantee success simply by running the suit because West might choose to discard on the clubs, voiding himself of diamonds. Then, declarer would have no way of getting the diamond trick he needs.

Therefore, declarer must get his diamond trick home first. He should take the ace of diamonds at Trick 6. (If West ruffs, too bad, but there was nothing to be done about it.) After that, declarer plays on clubs. If West never ruffs, declarer pitches all the remaining diamonds from the North hand, then picks up West's trumps. If West ruffs high at some point and plays a spade, declarer ruffs in dummy, and draws the last trump; if West ruffs low, declarer overruffs and plays a diamond to the queen.

SOLUTION 10

North
♠ A K J 2
♡ Q 10
◊ 7 6 4 3
♣ 9 8 5

West
♠ 8
♡ 8 7
◊ Q J 10 9
♣ K J 6 4 3 2

East
♠ Q 10 9 6 5 4
♡ 6 3 2
◊ 8
♣ Q 10 7

South
♠ 7 3
♡ A K J 9 5 4
◊ A K 5 2
♣ A

6♡ by South
Lead: ♠ *8*

This is a deal on which good general technique may be very important, even though you may not see the need for it when you begin the play. Can you see why? We'll get back to this point later on. Declarer should win the spade lead in dummy, lead a club to his ace, and play a heart to dummy's ten. If hearts prove to be five-zero, declarer should draw trumps and attack diamonds. If no one shows out on the first heart, declarer can afford to ruff a club before playing a heart back to dummy's queen. If hearts prove to be 4-1, declarer should draw trumps (returning to the closed hand with the diamond ace to do so), and attack diamonds.

However, if hearts are 3-2, declarer can afford to ruff dummy's last club before drawing the last trump, since that still leaves him with one more trump. Now declarer tests diamonds with the ace and king. If diamonds break, declarer gives up a diamond trick and claims. If East has four diamonds, declarer strip-squeezes him by playing the last trump. For his last three cards, East must keep two spades and only one diamond (he gets thrown in), or fewer spades (dummy's spades are good). If West turns out to have four diamonds, declarer must hope that East is down to all spades. Here's where all the preliminary moves, designed mainly to strip East of clubs, will pay off. South cashes the last trump and ducks a spade to East, making the last two tricks in dummy. And here's where your good general technique pays off also. You did play the seven of spades to Trick 1, didn't you? Do you see what an alert East can do to you otherwise?

SOLUTION 11

North
- ♠ 4 3 2
- ♡ A K 4 3
- ◇ 7 5 4
- ♣ K 4 3

West
- ♠ 5
- ♡ J 8 6
- ◇ Q 10 9 8 2
- ♣ 10 7 5 2

East
- ♠ A Q J 10 9 7
- ♡ Q 2
- ◇ 6 3
- ♣ Q J 9

South
- ♠ K 8 6
- ♡ 10 9 7 5
- ◇ A K J
- ♣ A 8 6

4♡ by South
Lead: ♠5

A. Your chances in four hearts are not very good. You first have to pick up the diamonds without loss, by finessing; then, you must work an endplay. The choice of endplay should depend on what you learn about East's distribution as you cash three rounds of diamonds. East is known to have started with six spades and two hearts. If he follows to three rounds of diamonds, he can't have three clubs; so, cash two top clubs and play any black card. If East shows up with the singleton or doubleton queen of diamonds, he has at least three clubs. The only hope is to run the diamonds, then try three rounds of clubs, hoping West will win the third one.

B. You'd be well placed as declarer at three hearts if only the opponents would let you peek at their cards. Since they won't do that, you need to find a line that takes advantage of as many distributions as possible. Here's one idea: Cash the tops in both minors. If East shows up with a void or singleton in either minor, play a third round of the other minor — the opponents won't be able to separate all their tricks. If East follows low to all four minor winners, exit with a club. This loses when East was dealt three diamonds to the queen and two clubs, but succeeds in all other cases. We hope this turns out to be the best play, because if it is, and East held 6-2-3-2 with the queen of diamonds, it would be possible to make four hearts with correct play yet be set at three hearts with best play.

SOLUTION 12

North
- ♠ 5 4
- ♡ K Q 3 2
- ◊ K Q 6 2
- ♣ K J 7

West
- ♠ Q J 10 7 6 3 2
- ♡ 4
- ◊ J 9 8 4
- ♣ 6

East
- ♠ —
- ♡ J 10 9 7 5
- ◊ 10 7
- ♣ 9 8 5 4 3 2

South
- ♠ A K 9 8
- ♡ A 8 6
- ◊ A 5 3
- ♣ A Q 10

6NT by South
Lead: ♠ Q

The bad spade break gives you an enormous amount of information, and the contract is assured with careful play. Here's one way to work it:

Win the first trick, and play the ace, king of hearts. If West turns out to have no hearts or one heart (see diagram), switch to high diamonds. Now, if West has fewer than three diamonds, finish the red-suit tops, keeping count of West's spades. (When West keeps three spades, cash clubs, then play the spade eight; when West keeps fewer than three spades, establish an extra spade trick.)

If West has more than three diamonds, duck a heart to East, win the return, and play winners to squeeze West between the pointed suits. If West follows to the first two high hearts, play a third high heart. When hearts split 3-3, there are twelve tricks. When West started with two hearts, play top diamonds. If West guards diamonds, lose a heart to East and squeeze West in the pointed suits. If East guards diamonds, work the spade endplay against West described in the previous paragraph. If West has four (or more) hearts, play ace, king, queen of diamonds until West shows out. Lose a diamond trick to East, win the return, and finish the minors to squeeze West between the majors.

North
- ♠ A 6
- ♡ Q J 5 2
- ◇ K 10 8 7
- ♣ 9 4 3

West
- ♠ Q 10 8 4 2
- ♡ 6
- ◇ Q 9 5 2
- ♣ 10 7 5

East
- ♠ K J 9 7
- ♡ 8 7 3
- ◇ J 3
- ♣ J 8 6 2

South
- ♠ 5 3
- ♡ A K 10 9 4
- ◇ A 6 4
- ♣ A K Q

6♡ by South
Lead: ♠4

You should win the opening lead and draw trumps. If trumps break 4-0, the only reasonable hope is that diamonds can be picked up without loss. Looking at the diamond suit alone, the best way to accomplish this is to cash the ace, intending to finesse if East drops an honor (which picks up queen-jack doubleton with West, or a singleton honor with East). However, if it is East who is void of trumps it is wiser to play him for queen-jack doubleton of diamonds, should that opportunity arise.

Against any other trump split, your plan should be to eliminate clubs, then throw the opponents on lead with a spade, forcing them to break diamonds (or concede a ruff-sluff). Competent defenders will defeat the contract any time their diamonds are 3-3: if either defender has queen-jack, his partner will win the spade, to lead a diamond. If the queen and jack are split, West will either lead his honor or play it on East's low lead. You can succeed only if West holds singleton-honor (then you must cash the ace or king before the endplay), or queen-jack doubleton, or honor-nine doubleton; otherwise, East must be void, or hold singleton honor, queen-jack doubleton, or honor-small where 'small' is not the nine.

The last possibility incorporates six cases, so that is the one you should play for. Thus, if West wins the spade and leads a diamond honor, or if East wins the spade and leads low to West's diamond honor, try for the drop next; if East leads a diamond honor, finesse next. You succeed when East has honor-small, or you get home if East has a singleton honor or a void, or if West has queen-jack doubleton.

SOLUTION 14

North
♠ A Q J 5 2
♡ A 7
◇ Q 7
♣ A 8 6 4

West
♠ 9 6 3
♡ 10 5 2
◇ 9 8 3
♣ Q 10 9 2

East
♠ K 8 4
♡ J 6 4 3
◇ K 10
♣ K J 7 5

South
♠ 10 7
♡ K Q 9 8
◇ A J 6 5 4 2
♣ 3

6◇ by South
Lead: ♠6

Don't give up! The 'impossible' simply takes a little longer — mentally longer, that is. You can avoid a trump loser with an elopement, provided that the final eloping comes late enough to force an opponent to waste a trump by underruffing. For example, suppose you were able to finesse the diamond jack, ruff safely four times in the South hand, and wind up in a two-card ending: singleton diamond queen and a spade in dummy, opposite singleton diamond ace and a heart in your hand. If East has the diamond king and a heart, you can crossruff the last two tricks.

You would like to be able to follow that general line, because if the diamond finesse loses you need not risk an extra undertrick trying to set up your fancy ending; however, it requires five entries to dummy (four for ruffs, one to finesse in diamonds), and there are only four. So, you must find East with exactly 3-4-2-4 distribution and the king of diamonds. Your entire line of play is virtually forced: Win the spade in dummy at Trick 2, ruff a spade, club ace, club ruff, heart ace, club ruff, heart king, heart ruff with dummy's seven. This leaves, you hope, something like:

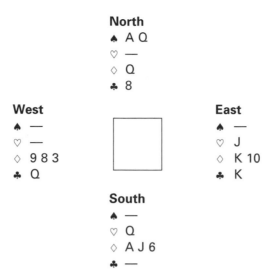

North
♠ A Q
♡ —
◇ Q
♣ 8

West
♠ —
♡ —
◇ 9 8 3
♣ Q

East
♠ —
♡ J
◇ K 10
♣ K

South
♠ —
♡ Q
◇ A J 6
♣ —

You lead the last club from dummy, and crossruff.

SOLUTION 15

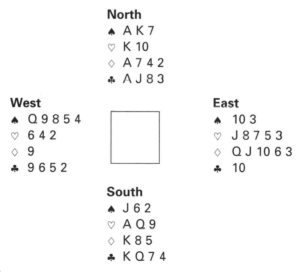

North
♠ A K 7
♡ K 10
◇ A 7 4 2
♣ A J 8 3

West
♠ Q 9 8 5 4
♡ 6 4 2
◇ 9
♣ 9 6 5 2

East
♠ 10 3
♡ J 8 7 5 3
◇ Q J 10 6 3
♣ 10

South
♠ J 6 2
♡ A Q 9
◇ K 8 5
♣ K Q 7 4

6♣ by South
Lead: ♣2

Every line has dangers. A simple play that takes only minimal risks (might fail if West has a void, or a total of two or three cards in diamonds and a major) is to play to the ◇K, then towards the ◇A, planning to give up a diamond. The idea is to ruff dummy's last diamond with the ♣K, then finesse in clubs to return to dummy and draw trumps. Other plans are defeated by more likely holdings. For example, trying to ruff a spade in dummy may fail if West is short in either major.

SOLUTION 16

North
- ♠ A 9 6 4
- ♡ Q 10
- ◊ K J 8
- ♣ 7 5 3 2

West
- ♠ Q 8 3
- ♡ J 6 5 2
- ◊ 7
- ♣ A K 10 9 4

East
- ♠ 10 5 2
- ♡ A K 9 8 7 4
- ◊ 3
- ♣ Q J 6

South
- ♠ K J 7
- ♡ 3
- ◊ A Q 10 9 6 5 4 2
- ♣ 8

5◊ by South
Lead: ♣K

There is always the spade finesse, but you should not settle for that. If East has the ace-king of hearts (not unlikely, since West might have doubled five diamonds with his club strength and a high heart, plus whatever other high-card bits he may hold), you can avoid the spade finesse with a double squeeze. Admittedly you may have to guess what is going on in the ending, and you may even be deceived out of a successful finesse by tricky opponents. Still, even against expert defenders a competent declarer will guess right most of the time in endings of this type.

In any event, there is nothing to lose by starting to play for the squeeze — you can always change your mind later. First rectify the count. You must do that in clubs (if you ruff at Trick 2, draw trumps, and lead a heart to lose a trick, the opponents can lead a second heart to quash your heart menace) — so at Trick 2, discard a heart. Later, you draw trumps, ruff dummy's ten of hearts (to give East a chance to give you information), ruff a third round of clubs (to isolate the club menace against West; the play to Trick 2 strongly suggests that clubs are five-three — West probably did not shift because he thought his partner's club at Trick 1 might be a singleton). Then, run trumps, leaving yourself with:

North
♠ A 9
♡ Q
♢ —
♣ 7

South
♠ K J 7
♡ —
♢ 6
♣ —

You lead the six of diamonds. If, after West's discard to this trick, dummy's club is not high, you discard it. Then, you play a spade to the ace, lead another spade, and guess. The spade finesse is right only if West remains with a high club and a high heart for his last two cards. You won't always get the ending right, but you will have given yourself the best chance. For example, with the East-West cards as shown in the full-hand diagram, East might carelessly play the heart king when you lead the ten from dummy.

SOLUTION 17

North
- ♠ 7 5 4
- ♡ Q 8 5
- ◇ K 8 5 4 2
- ♣ J 6

West
- ♠ 9 8 3 2
- ♡ 3
- ◇ J 7 3
- ♣ 9 7 4 3 2

East
- ♠ A K 6
- ♡ K J 7
- ◇ Q 10 9 6
- ♣ K 10 8

South
- ♠ Q J 10
- ♡ A 10 9 6 4 2
- ◇ A
- ♣ A Q 5

4♡ by South
Lead: ♠2

While the correct play here is simple — unblock the ace of diamonds, lead the nine of hearts — it is easy to get careless.

First, let's look at the winning line. If West plays the jack of hearts, dummy covers with the queen; East, who is marked with all the missing major high cards, has no effective defense: if he leaves you in dummy, you can do your minor-suit work at once; if he captures the heart queen, the heart eight will serve as a later entry. When West plays low and East wins with the heart jack, the defense is no better off. East must let you reach dummy to take a trump finesse (which provides its own reentry), then to pitch a club on the diamond king, and take a club finesse. East will be able to defeat the contract, by allowing your nine of hearts to win, only if he started with four spades or four hearts. In all other cases, when he lets the heart nine hold you will endplay him, with ace and another heart.

Note what may happen if declarer starts instead with a heart to dummy's eight. East, if he holds king-jack-seven of hearts, can win and return a diamond. This gives declarer an entry to dummy, but what does South play to the trick from the closed hand? Nothing works out. If declarer ruffs, he never gets to dummy. If declarer pitches a club, he has no club-ruff reentry to dummy after taking the club finesse. If declarer wins in dummy and plays trumps, East can cover, later taking the setting trick with the king of clubs.

North
- ♠ 7 5 3 2
- ♡ Q 9 8
- ◇ 5 3 2
- ♣ A 10 7

West
- ♠ Q
- ♡ K J 10 7 6 4
- ◇ 9 8 4
- ♣ K Q J

East
- ♠ J 10 9 8
- ♡ A 5 3 2
- ◇ 7
- ♣ 9 5 4 3

South
- ♠ A K 6 4
- ♡ —
- ◇ A K Q J 10 6
- ♣ 8 6 2

4♠ by South
Lead: ♡ J

If you ruff the opening lead and cash the ace-king of spades, you are down whenever trumps break 4-1, even in the very unlikely event that the opponent with four spades also has three diamonds. You can give yourself a much better chance by ruffing the opening lead, drawing only one round of trumps, then switching to diamonds. If someone ruffs and: (a) plays a trump back, you win and continue diamonds, keeping control; (b) plays a heart, you ruff and continue diamonds, keeping the second high spade for an entry; (c) plays a club, you win dummy's ace, draw another round of trumps, and continue diamonds, throwing clubs from dummy if given the opportunity. In (c), the contract can be defeated if an opponent started with four spades and at most one diamond (see diagram), but only after best defense — and nothing has been lost by the line of play chosen.

If no one ruffs diamonds for a while, throw clubs from dummy. On any normal distribution of the opponents' cards, they will be able to take only three trump tricks.

SOLUTION 19

North
- ♠ A Q 5 2
- ♡ J 7
- ◇ A Q 9 2
- ♣ A 8 7

West
- ♠ K 9
- ♡ K 9 6 2
- ◇ K 10 6 5 4
- ♣ J 6

East
- ♠ 10 8 4 3
- ♡ 10 5 4 3
- ◇ J 8 7 3
- ♣ Q

South
- ♠ J 7 6
- ♡ A Q 8
- ◇ —
- ♣ K 10 9 5 4 3 2

6♣ by South
Lead: ♣6

There are not enough dummy entries to eliminate diamonds effectively, so you must content yourself with one diamond ruff (without cashing the diamond ace, because you would not know what to discard). Even so, there is a good chance to endplay West — if he has the king of diamonds, a diamond exit is not safe for him.

To maximize the chance of getting West's help while preserving all normal chances (finesses in both spades and hearts, a 3-3 break in spades), you should win the club king, cash the club ace, then ruff dummy's deuce of diamonds (mainly to give East a chance to put up the king). Now is the time to play the majors; the most effective way is ace of spades, then low towards the jack. This makes the contract when, (a), East has the spade king: if he plays it, there are two discards for hearts; if he ducks, you win the spade jack, get to dummy with a trump, pitch a spade on the diamond ace and lose at most one heart; and, (b), when spades break 3-3: if West captures the spade jack and leads a diamond to the queen and king, you ruff, then test spades before risking the heart finesse; and, (c), West has king-doubleton of spades plus the king of diamonds (he is endplayed); and, (d), when the heart finesse wins.

It is almost as good to win two clubs ending in the closed hand and play a spade to dummy's queen, intending to refuse the heart finesse and play for a squeeze if the spade finesse loses.

North
- ♠ 7 5 3
- ♡ A Q 6 4 2
- ◇ K 4 3
- ♣ K Q

West
- ♠ K 10 9
- ♡ 9 7 3
- ◇ 10 9 8 7 5 2
- ♣ 3

East
- ♠ Q J 4 2
- ♡ K J 10 8
- ◇ J 6
- ♣ J 7 4

South
- ♠ A 8 6
- ♡ 5
- ◇ A Q
- ♣ A 10 9 8 6 5 2

6♣ by South
Lead: ◇ 10

Should declarer take precautions against a 4-0 trump break? If so, he must do it right away because a trump-shortening process will wind up an entry short when declarer tests trumps before starting to take ruffs in the closed hand. To play for a trump reduction, declarer would try diamond ace-queen, heart ace, heart ruff, now a club to the king. If trumps are not 4-0, declarer can draw a second trump in dummy, take a spade discard, return to the South hand, and draw trumps. This line will succeed on most normal breaks. If East has four trumps, declarer sees the break when he leads to dummy's club king, cashes the diamond king, ruffs another heart, leads another club to dummy, takes another heart ruff (his third), exits with a spade and scores the last two tricks with the ace-ten of trumps. If West turns out to have four trumps, declarer still has the chance of dropping the heart king tripleton for a discard of his second spade loser.

Compared to leaving hearts alone, keeping the finesse in reserve, the early ruffout loses when West has four trumps and four (or more) hearts to the king. This is less likely than the case in which leaving hearts alone loses, when East has four trumps and the heart finesse loses. However, these possibilities deal with fractions of a 4-0 trump break, which is rather unlikely to begin with. Starting the trump-reduction plan immediately gives up the heart finesse, so it also loses when a defender has three trumps and two diamonds (see diagram), which is more likely than the losing cases dealing with 4-0 trump splits. So, this is a deal on which the fancy play should be rejected. The correct play is for declarer simply to take his twelve top tricks.

SOLUTION 21

North
- ♠ K 8 7 6
- ♡ A 9 6 3
- ◇ A K 3
- ♣ A 7

West
- ♠ 5 2
- ♡ Q 7 5
- ◇ 8 2
- ♣ K J 10 5 3 2

East
- ♠ 4
- ♡ J 10 8 4
- ◇ Q J 10 9 6
- ♣ Q 9 4

South
- ♠ A Q J 10 9 3
- ♡ K 2
- ◇ 7 5 4
- ♣ 8 6

6♠ by South
Lead: ◇ 8

East's double gives you useful information for the play, but the opening lead, attacking dummy's diamond entries, is detrimental. For example, suppose you try for a heart-diamond squeeze by winning the opening lead, drawing trumps, then losing a trick in clubs to rectify the count. The defense will return a diamond to knock out dummy's second diamond honor. This will reduce you to finding one opponent (presumably East) with five or more diamonds plus either five-plus hearts or the queen-jack-ten. In contrast, if West had led, say, a club, you could have won, drawn trumps, lost a club to rectify the count, won the diamond return in dummy, then run trumps, throwing the diamond three from dummy. On the next-to-last trump an opponent with five diamonds and four hearts (or the queen-jack-ten) would have been trump-squeezed. You might have had to guess the distribution, but this is relatively easy, as such guesses go.

Regretting what might have been after a different lead is profitless. Your best move depends on West's skill level. Against an ordinary West, it is probably best to draw trumps, lead a heart from dummy, and pass it. West is likely to continue diamonds, after which you can clear the remaining red-suit tops and run trumps to effect a double squeeze when West is long in hearts. However, a capable West with long hearts will be able to see that squeeze coming and will break it up by shifting to clubs when he wins his heart trick. Against such a West, you are better off not rectifying the count. You hope East has four hearts and five diamonds, not such a longshot. After the king of diamonds and six rounds of trumps, your hands will look like this:

North
♠ —
♡ A 9 6 3
◇ A
♣ A

South
♠ —
♡ K 2
◇ 7 5
♣ 8 6

East must keep at least two diamonds and, you hope, at least four hearts; he must give up one of those cards when you lead a club to dummy's ace. If he keeps four hearts, the diamonds are good. If he keeps fewer than four hearts, you lead a heart to the king and another heart, intending to duck the trick to East if possible. (You can work the avoidance successfully as long as East has at least two of the three missing heart honors. If West plays his honor on the second round, you play ace and another.) Note that it is still possible to make the slam on this line when East was dealt queen-jack-ten tripleton of hearts.

SOLUTION 22

North
- ♠ J 6 3
- ♡ 10 9 8
- ◇ Q 10 9 4
- ♣ K 10 3

West
- ♠ 8 5
- ♡ K Q 7 3 2
- ◇ 5 3 2
- ♣ 8 7 4

East
- ♠ K 10 9 7
- ♡ A J 6 4
- ◇ 8 7
- ♣ 9 5 2

South
- ♠ A Q 4 2
- ♡ 5
- ◇ A K J 6
- ♣ A Q J 6

4♠ by South
Lead: ♡ K

No doubt partner should have bid five diamonds, not four spades, but that's his problem. Your problem is a bit more complex.

You should begin by ruffing at Trick 2, entering dummy, and leading a spade to the queen. If West wins with the king and plays another heart, you should ruff, unblock the spade ace, enter dummy, then cash the spade jack. This succeeds when spades are 3-3, or when the defender with four spades has only three hearts. Paradoxically, even though heart forces represent the main danger to your contract, if West does not force you to ruff a heart you should ruff one yourself, to remove the third heart from the hand of a defender with four trumps.

If the spade queen holds, you have a choice. You could cash the spade ace, then smile if the king drops. If the king doesn't drop, you turn your attention to the minors, hoping for a 3-3 spade break. The opponents can make their trumps separately, but they can't draw your trumps or take any further heart tricks. This is clearly better than leading a low spade after winning the queen — that loses when East started with king-doubleton of spades.

However, an even better chance is to leave spades alone after winning the spade queen, turning your attention instead to the minors. Suppose you continue the minor you entered dummy with earlier, planning to play that suit until an opponent ruffs, or both opponents are out (then you switch to the other minor; perhaps you can win the sixth minor-suit trick in dummy, and ruff the last heart). What could go wrong?

If spades are 3-3, the opponents cannot do anything effective (you will cash the spade ace as soon as possible after an opponent ruffs). If spades are 4-2, the opponents are helpless (see diagram) except in the unlikely case where the player short in trumps gets a ruff. The suggested play would lose, as compared with playing the spade ace after the queen, if one opponent had four spades and three hearts — East-West would get a ruff with their short trump hand. However, this is less likely to have been dealt, and is further contraindicated by West's pass over one diamond (at favorable vulnerability, he might have preempted with six hearts to the king-queen).

SOLUTION 23

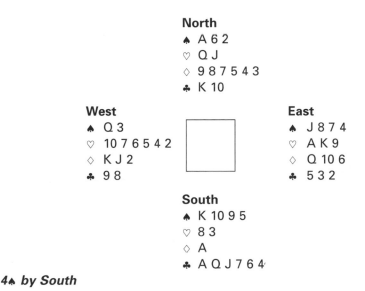

North
- ♠ A 6 2
- ♡ Q J
- ◊ 9 8 7 5 4 3
- ♣ K 10

West
- ♠ Q 3
- ♡ 10 7 6 5 4 2
- ◊ K J 2
- ♣ 9 8

East
- ♠ J 8 7 4
- ♡ A K 9
- ◊ Q 10 6
- ♣ 5 3 2

South
- ♠ K 10 9 5
- ♡ 8 3
- ◊ A
- ♣ A Q J 7 6 4

4♠ by South
Lead: ♡ 5

If spades are 3-3, your play to this trick very likely doesn't matter. And if West started with four spades, or East started with five, you can kiss the contract goodbye in any event. The crucial cases, therefore, are where East started with four spades, and has no more hearts (when East has another heart, you can make the contract only if East failed to split spade honors, which would have been an elementary blunder).

Assuming East was dealt four spades and three hearts, there are two good reasons to go up with the king of spades at Trick 6. First, East is more likely to have been dealt one honor (eight cases) than two honors (six cases). Second, if East did start with exactly three hearts, he misdefended when he led his third heart. It would be easier for East to see the correct defense when he held both spade honors; his mistake is more likely from one honor.

SOLUTION 24

North
- ♠ K 8 6 2
- ♡ 6 5 4 3
- ◇ K Q
- ♣ 10 7 6

West
- ♠ 10 9 7
- ♡ 10 9
- ◇ A J 7 5 4
- ♣ 9 4 3

East
- ♠ Q J
- ♡ K Q J 8
- ◇ 10 9 6 3
- ♣ 8 5 2

South
- ♠ A 5 4 3
- ♡ A 7 2
- ◇ 8 2
- ♣ A K Q J

4♠ by South
Lead: ♡ 10

The only chance to avoid two heart losers is an endplay, and the only available throw-in suit is trumps. Therefore, one opponent, presumably West, must hold one or two hearts, exactly three trumps (for the throw-in), and the ace of diamonds (so that his partner cannot cash heart tricks). Your plan should be to win an early heart trick, knock out the ace of diamonds, win the return, draw two rounds of trumps, cash the second diamond, and run clubs. If the opponent to be endplayed refuses to ruff, after finishing the clubs you put him in with a trump.

The question is which round of hearts to win. If the lead is from a doubleton, you must duck the first trick. However, if you duck the first trick when the lead is a singleton, your heart ace will be ruffed away at Trick 2. The doubleton is more likely to have been dealt, but East's play at Trick 1 suggests that the lead is a singleton: if East held king-queen-jack-eight, he could not overtake at Trick 1 without giving up trick-taking power in the suit. But wait! On the auction, East is safe to overtake because he knows South doesn't have four hearts. So there is no reliable inference to be drawn from East's play at Trick 1 — not even if it is the same East from the previous deal. So, you should stick with the percentage play of ducking at Trick 1 to set up your endplay.

North
♠ A K 5 3 2
♡ A K 8 7 4
◇ 3 2
♣ 8

West
♠ J 9
♡ 9 2
◇ J 10 9 8 7 5
♣ A 6 2

East
♠ Q 10 4
♡ Q J 10 6
◇ Q 6 4
♣ 5 4 3

South
♠ 8 7 6
♡ 5 3
◇ A K
♣ K Q J 10 9 7

6NT by South
Lead: ◇ J

There are only eleven tricks, so someone overbid. You and partner can work out who it was. But that should come later — right now, your objective is to make your slam. The twelfth trick can come only from a major-suit squeeze — one opponent must hold at least three spades and at least four hearts. Even if West's methods allow him to open two diamonds with that holding, the chance that he was dealt so many major-suit cards with his long diamonds is negligible. It is virtually certain that the squeeze can operate only against East.

If East is to be the victim, a preliminary move is necessary. Simply knocking out the ace of clubs and running minor-suit winners will not do, because dummy will be squeezed ahead of East. Instead, North's spade winners must first be cleared away (technically a Vienna Coup), to give force to the spade menace in the South hand. Then, the squeeze will function. Since the defense will get in with the ace of clubs, and a diamond return at that point will remove the last entry to the South hand, the spade winners must be cashed immediately, before playing on clubs. If East has the ace of clubs, too bad.

SOLUTION 26

North
- ♠ Q J 9
- ♡ K 9 7 3 2
- ◇ K 4
- ♣ 7 6 4

West
- ♠ 10 6
- ♡ Q 10 4
- ◇ Q 10 6 2
- ♣ A 8 5 3

East
- ♠ K 8 7 3
- ♡ A 6 5
- ◇ J 9 7 5 3
- ♣ 2

South
- ♠ A 5 4 2
- ♡ J 8
- ◇ A 8
- ♣ K Q J 10 9

3NT by South
Lead: ◇ 2

You have seven top tricks, and no time to go after hearts. Therefore, the extra tricks must come from spades. Not only must the finesse win but you must pick up a third-round trick in the suit as well. This means that you must find East with the king of spades short, or West with the ten of spades short. You must choose to play for one or the other.

It is in your interest to delay the decision in spades as long as possible, so you can decide whom to play for shorter spades based on as much information as possible. Therefore, you should win the first trick with the ace of diamonds (leaving the king of diamonds as an entry to take the spade finesse), and play a club from the closed hand. You would like to win the first club trick (so as to see a 4-1 club break before being forced to use dummy's king of diamonds), so either the queen or nine of clubs (depending on your opinion of left-hand opponent) is likely to be best. When it comes time to make the spade decision, you will use whatever clues have come to light from the minors.

North
- ♠ A 4 3
- ♡ 9 4 3 2
- ◊ 8 6
- ♣ A K 8 4

West
- ♠ Q 7 6 2
- ♡ J 7
- ◊ 5 3
- ♣ Q 10 7 5 2

East
- ♠ —
- ♡ 10 8 6
- ◊ A Q J 10 9 4 2
- ♣ J 9 6

South
- ♠ K J 10 9 8 5
- ♡ A K Q 5
- ◊ K 7
- ♣ 3

6♠ by South
Lead: ◊ 5

Suppose you cash the spade king, all following low, then lead the spade jack; and suppose West follows with the remaining small spade. What would be your best play to pick up spades? The finesse, because East would be known to have eight cards in diamonds and small spades, while West started with only four of them.

The question is not whether to finesse but when. If you cash the spade king first, you cannot pick up all four spades with West. If you run the jack of spades first you handle the 4-0 split, but you lose to East's singleton queen. Assuming the bidding would be the same in each case, which is more likely for East to hold, a spade void or a singleton queen? If East holds singleton queen, he has five cards in hearts and clubs, which were dealt from the thirteen cards the defenders hold in those suits. If East is void in spades, he has six cards out of the thirteen heart-club cards. The latter is more likely to have been dealt because it is closer to an even split of the heart-club cards. Therefore, a first-round spade finesse is better than a second-round finesse.

What about playing the side suits first to get more information? Clearly it is too dangerous to play hearts. There is also some danger in playing clubs. East might ruff the first round; and if you try the club ace-king, East may ruff from 1-4-7-1. What about one high club and one low club? If East shows out, spade king and (unless West drops the queen) spade ace is now the percentage play. If East follows to the second club, the best play in spades is still to run the jack. This now fails if East started with 3-1-7-2 and three small spades. These tiny chances are probably not worth computing.

SOLUTION 28

North
- ♠ A K 6
- ♡ A K 3
- ◇ 9 3
- ♣ A 7 5 3 2

West
- ♠ Q 10 7 5
- ♡ 10 9 8
- ◇ 10 7 6 5 4
- ♣ Q

East
- ♠ J 9 8 4 3 2
- ♡ 5 4
- ◇ 8
- ♣ K J 10 9

South
- ♠ —
- ♡ Q J 7 6 2
- ◇ A K Q J 2
- ♣ 8 6 4

7♡ by South
Lead: ♡ 10

There are two ways you might overcome a bad diamond break. If an opponent with five (or six) diamonds has the long trump, you can ruff a diamond in dummy, then return to the closed hand with a spade ruff to draw the last trump. Alternatively, if an opponent with five (or six) diamonds has four (or five) clubs, you can cash dummy's top spades, draw trumps, test for the singleton diamond ten, then finish the trumps for a minor-suit squeeze.

Which is better? If one opponent has a preponderance of the missing diamonds, that defender will have been dealt three of the missing five hearts more often than four of the missing five clubs. Therefore, the ruff possibility is the better chance. You should cash one high diamond at Trick 3 and, if the ten does not drop, continue with another high diamond. If both opponents follow twice, draw the last trump and claim. If someone shows out and does not ruff, you can ruff your diamond loser in dummy, ruff the spade six to get back to the South hand, draw the last trump, and claim.

North
- ♠ 8 7 3 2
- ♡ Q 10 6
- ◊ A K
- ♣ J 9 5 4

West
- ♠ 4
- ♡ 7 5 2
- ◊ 9 8 6 5 4
- ♣ 10 7 6 2

East
- ♠ K J 10 9 6 5
- ♡ A
- ◊ J 10 3
- ♣ Q 8 3

South
- ♠ A Q
- ♡ K J 9 8 4 3
- ◊ Q 7 2
- ♣ A K

6♡ by South
Lead: 4♠

It looks as if you should have bid six notrump. Meanwhile, is there anything you can do to avoid a spade ruff? West might have started with a singleton (or void) in hearts, but that is a really long shot. There is a decent chance, however, that East started with a singleton ace of hearts. In that case, if a club trick can be established in dummy it can be used to pitch South's remaining winning spade (whether East ruffs your winning club or not).

There is virtually no risk in this line: win the spade, cash the club ace-king, enter dummy with a diamond, ruff the nine of clubs (bringing down ten-third in the West hand wouldn't do much good). Then, if East's queen has dropped, play another diamond to dummy, and the winning club, discarding a spade.

SOLUTION 30

North
- ♠ A 10 8 5 3
- ♡ K 7 4
- ◇ Q J
- ♣ 9 6 2

West
- ♠ J 4 2
- ♡ 10 8
- ◇ 10 9 8 5
- ♣ Q 10 8 3

East
- ♠ Q 9 7 6
- ♡ 9 5 2
- ◇ 7 6 4 3 2
- ♣ J

South
- ♠ K
- ♡ A Q J 6 3
- ◇ A K
- ♣ A K 7 5 4

6♡ by South
Lead: ◇ 10

The main worry is a 4-1 club break. There is a chance to do something about it, by ruffing a club in dummy, perhaps with the king of hearts. If East has the four clubs, West will get a ruff if you don't draw his trumps. You can't get a ruff if you draw three rounds to exhaust West, or even if you can exhaust West with two rounds (East will get in with a club to lead a third round).

Success is more likely if West has the long clubs. Suppose you win the diamond lead, cash one high club, overtake the spade king in dummy, and lead a second club. If East has a singleton club and two or three trumps, he has no effective defense — you will get a club ruff to make the contract.

This plan can be improved a little. What about drawing one round of trumps early, just in case East is 4-4 in the rounded suits? You cannot take that round with dummy's king (you need the king for your club ruff if East started with three hearts and one club — see diagram). So, draw one round of trumps with an honor from the closed hand, cash one high club, overtake the spade king, and lead another club. If East started with four hearts and four clubs, you win the second club, lose the third round of clubs, win the return, ruff a club, unblock the heart king if necessary, return safely to the closed hand and draw trumps. (This will also work if West was 4-4 in hearts and clubs.)

SOLUTION 31

North
- ♠ K Q 4 3
- ♡ K Q J
- ◇ 9 8
- ♣ Q J 9 4

West
- ♠ 5
- ♡ A 10 9
- ◇ A K Q 10 6 3
- ♣ K 10 8

East
- ♠ J 7 2
- ♡ 8 7 5 4 3 2
- ◇ 5
- ♣ 7 5 2

South
- ♠ A 10 9 8 6
- ♡ 6
- ◇ J 7 4 2
- ♣ A 6 3

4♠ by South
Lead: ◇ K

Since West has only six diamonds, it is very likely he holds both the ace of hearts and king of clubs for his bidding. Therefore, you must plan to discard two clubs on dummy's hearts. Since the only entry to the hearts is in trumps, you must take a position about the lie of the spades. If spades are 2-2, the winning line is to ruff the diamond high in dummy, draw trumps, and concede a trick to the ace of hearts. If West has a singleton small trump, however, that plan will fail, because you won't be able to enjoy dummy's heart winners.

On the bidding, the second trump position is considerably more likely than the first, so the percentage play is to ruff the diamond high in dummy at Trick 3 and take an immediate finesse against the jack of spades. If this succeeds, lead a heart. West will probably win his ace of hearts and play another diamond. You can ruff high in dummy, cash two heart tricks for club discards, then repeat the trump finesse. In addition to catering to a small singleton spade with West, this line will succeed if West has two small trumps provided he also has at least three hearts. If East had started with only five hearts, he could have discarded hearts successfully. It would have been a stronger defense to throw a heart from his actual hand. This would have given you a more difficult problem.

SOLUTION 32

North
♠ A Q J 3
♡ A 5
◇ A K 7 2
♣ Q J 5

West
♠ 10 6 4 2
♡ J 9 8 6 3
◇ J
♣ 7 3 2

East
♠ 8 7 5
♡ K 10 2
◇ Q 10 9 4 3
♣ 8 4

South
♠ K 9
♡ Q 7 4
◇ 8 6 5
♣ A K 10 9 6

7♣ by South
Lead: ♣2

Start by drawing trumps. (a) If trumps are 3-2, cash the ace-king of diamonds. Then:

(a1) If both follow, or if East shows out, cash four spades throwing a diamond and a heart, ruff a diamond, and (if diamonds were not 3-3), play the last trump to squeeze West when he started with long diamonds and the heart king.

(a2) If West shows out (see diagram), so that the play in (a1) is doomed to failure, return to the spade king, cash a club to pitch a heart from dummy, and run spades to reach:

♠ —
♡ A
◇ 7 2
♣ —

♠ —
♡ Q 7
◇ —
♣ 10

When East started with the heart king, he will be squeezed. If he keeps two diamonds, cash the heart ace; if not, play diamonds.

(b) If trumps are 4-1, discard a heart from dummy on the fourth club, run four spades and two diamonds to reach the same ending as above. Here, the count may be unknown, forcing you to guess.

SOLUTION 33

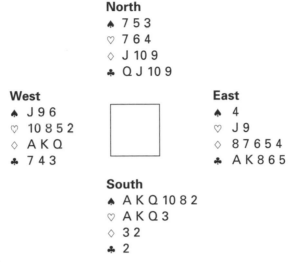

North
♠ 7 5 3
♡ 7 6 4
♢ J 10 9
♣ Q J 10 9

West
♠ J 9 6
♡ 10 8 5 2
♢ A K Q
♣ 7 4 3

East
♠ 4
♡ J 9
♢ 8 7 6 5 4
♣ A K 8 6 5

South
♠ A K Q 10 8 2
♡ A K Q 3
♢ 3 2
♣ 2

4♠ by South
Lead: ◇ *K*

Your basic plan should be to try to ruff a heart in dummy. When you gain the lead you will draw two rounds of trumps. When trumps are 2-2, claim. When trumps are three-one, you will switch to hearts, making the contract if hearts are 3-3, or if the opponent with long hearts also has the remaining trump. (If West shows out on the first trump, you will switch to hearts at once, hoping to use a heart ruff as the dummy entry for the trump finesse.)

A trap to avoid along the way is the possibility of an overruff. Suppose West has three spades to the jack and long hearts, as in the diagram. If you ruff at Trick 3 and proceed with the basic plan, your heart ruff will come off smoothly. But the rest of the play will not be so carefree. Dummy will remain with all clubs. East will surely be able to win a club and may be able to give West an overruff. To avoid this danger, you should discard your losing club at Trick 3. Then, West can get an overruff only if he has a singleton or void in clubs.

SOLUTION 34

North
- ♠ A 9 8 3
- ♡ Q 6 2
- ◇ 5 4
- ♣ K J 10 7

West
- ♠ K 10 5 2
- ♡ 8 4 3
- ◇ A J 9
- ♣ 6 4 2

East
- ♠ Q J 6 4
- ♡ A 5
- ◇ K 10 7 3 2
- ♣ 9 8

South
- ♠ 7
- ♡ K J 10 9 7
- ◇ Q 8 6
- ♣ A Q 5 3

3♡ by South
Lead: ♡ 4

West didn't choose his trump lead because he is loaded in your second suit, clubs; he probably would have led a spade from a strong sequence. So, East, who passed originally, has a high spade as well as his ace of hearts; he won't hold ace-king of diamonds — the queen of diamonds will not stand up. And the opponents will surely be able to stop any attempt to ruff a diamond in dummy.

Since the diamonds are all going to be losers if you draw trumps, you won't mind if the opponents ruff one of your club winners — the trick will come back when you ruff the third diamond in dummy. So, try a dummy reversal for an overtrick: win Trick 2 in the closed hand, play spade ace, spade ruff, club to dummy, spade ruff, club to dummy, spade ruff, club to dummy. The chances are that the long-trump opponent will be short in clubs, and will ruff one of the club leads to dummy. However, if one opponent is long in both clubs and hearts, all three club leads to get to dummy will succeed; the third time you are there you can draw the last trump, to make ten tricks.

North
♠ A 6 2
♡ J 9 8 7
♢ J 10 8
♣ 7 6 3

West
♠ 9
♡ K Q 10 6 4
♢ Q 5 4 3 2
♣ J 9

East
♠ K Q J 8
♡ A 5 3 2
♢ 9 7 6
♣ 10 4

South
♠ 10 7 5 4 3
♡ —
♢ A K
♣ A K Q 8 5 2

4♠ by South
Lead: ♡K

A. Overtricks might be available if trumps are 3-2, but there is no need to take any chances against a 4-1 trump break. Plan to cash the spade ace and play on clubs, making exactly ten tricks in most cases. A small improvement is to start with a high club at Trick 2. If all follow, play the spade ace and more clubs. If someone ruffs the first club, ruff the heart return, cash the spade ace, and continue clubs, eventually ruffing a club in dummy.

B. Playing in 5♣, if spades are 3-2 drawing trumps is best. But if spades are 4-1, it won't do you any good to play spades before clubs. Indeed, the opponents may be able to continue spades to their profit, overruffing dummy on the fourth round. Leading spades prematurely thus could cost the contract if the clubs are 2-2. The best move is simply to draw trumps and hope for a good break in one black suit or the other.

SOLUTION 36

North
- ♠ A 8 6 5 2
- ♡ A 5 4
- ♦ 6 3 2
- ♣ Q 7

West
- ♠ J
- ♡ J 9 8 6 2
- ♦ 8 7 4
- ♣ 9 5 4 2

East
- ♠ Q 10 9 7 3
- ♡ K 10 7
- ♦ —
- ♣ J 10 8 6 3

South
- ♠ K 4
- ♡ Q 3
- ♦ A K Q J 10 9 5
- ♣ A K

7◇ by South
Lead: ◇ 7

A. If East follows to the opening lead, the six of diamonds in dummy is an entry. You can get the thirteenth trick from spades against a 3-3 or 4-2 division: win the opening lead, draw the remaining trump, play spade king, spade ace, spade ruff (high), diamond to the six, spade ruff, heart ace, established spade. In addition, if West has five (or six) spades you can succeed with a squeeze when he also holds the heart king. Instead of re-entering dummy with the ace of hearts, simply finish the minor-suit winners in the closed hand, discarding correctly from dummy behind West on the squeeze trick.

B. If East shows out on the first trick, so that the six of diamonds is not an entry, ruffing out spades will succeed only when spades are 3-3. You must choose between that and playing for a spade-heart squeeze, which can succeed if either opponent has four or more spades plus the king of hearts. You need not make an early decision between these two lines. Instead, run winners to reach:

North
♠ A 8 6 5
♡ A
◇ —
♣ —

□

South
♠ K 4
♡ Q 3
◇ 5
♣ —

You can cash the king of spades (kept until now for deception), and next the ace of spades, but then must guess what to do. The minor-suit count may help your decision, and against most opponents it would be best to make the clubs the last winners cashed prior to reaching the ending shown.

SOLUTION 37

North
- ♠ A 3 2
- ♡ 9 5 4
- ◇ Q J 10
- ♣ 8 7 6 4

West
- ♠ J 10 9 8
- ♡ Q 6
- ◇ 8 4 3 2
- ♣ 9 5 3

East
- ♠ Q 6 5 4
- ♡ K 7 3 2
- ◇ 9 7 5
- ♣ 10 2

South
- ♠ K 7
- ♡ A J 10 8
- ◇ A K 6
- ♣ A K Q J

6NT by South
Lead: ♠ J

A. This type of set-up appears in many advanced textbooks. You need three tricks from hearts, and the percentage play is to keep on taking finesses. But dummy is short of entries, so you should win the first trick with dummy's ace of spades, to lead a low heart from the North hand, preserving the nine. The finesse of the jack loses, as expected. Later, after cashing a lot of winners, you re-enter dummy in diamonds and lead the nine of hearts, underplaying with the eight if East follows low. This allows the lead to remain in dummy for a third heart finesse.

B. The books never seem to cover the unexpected. What if the jack of hearts holds the trick? This will happen if East was dealt king-queen, or if West produces a clever (or accidental) hold-up. There are now four strategies declarer might adopt: (1) Cash the ace; this loses when East was dealt king-queen-fourth (six cases) or king-queen-fifth (four less likely cases). (2) Lead a low heart and, if East wins, later play for the drop. This loses when East was dealt honor-doubleton or king-queen-fourth (14 cases). (3) Lead a low heart and, if East wins, finesse later. This loses when East started with honor-doubleton (eight cases) or honor-third (12 more likely cases). (4) Get to dummy with a diamond and finesse again. This loses when East has honor-fourth (eight cases). In the real world, plays (1) and (2) are inferior, because they lose when no hold-up is involved. Most Wests would not hold up, and virtually none could do it smoothly enough to fool an alert South. Assuming West might hold up, play (4) is better than play (3), since it loses in fewer cases, and against harder hold-ups. A full answer requires determining the probability that West would hold up with various holdings. Anyway, after the jack of hearts holds declarer might as well run clubs. If clubs are skewed, the distributional information might help. Alternatively, the discards may make it safe to cash diamonds before making a commitment in hearts.

SOLUTION 38

North
- ♠ A K 2
- ♡ 9 5 4
- ♢ J 10 6
- ♣ 8 7 6 4

West
- ♠ J 10 9 8
- ♡ Q 6
- ♢ 8 4 3 2
- ♣ 9 5 3

East
- ♠ Q 6 5 4
- ♡ K 7 3 2
- ♢ 9 7 5
- ♣ 10 2

South
- ♠ 7 3
- ♡ A J 10 8
- ♢ A K Q
- ♣ A K Q J

6NT by South
Lead: ♠ J

A. In the expected case, this is not much different from part A of the previous problem. Declarer cannot guard against a many-trick set as in the previous problem, because early defensive spade leads will force him to play hearts before cashing minor-suit tricks.

B. This time, if the jack of hearts holds, declarer's options are more limited. The relatively attractive play (4), cashing winners safely, then using dummy's second entry to take a second heart finesse, is not an option because a second spade play to dummy will bare a loser. In this layout, it becomes even more important for declarer to judge the probability that West would refuse to capture the jack of hearts. If South assumes West would never duck, then play (3) is best. In contrast, if declarer believes West good enough always to duck, play (1) — undoubtedly the worst in virtually all practical situations — would be best. We think play (3), which is right when West will hold up infrequently, will turn out best in most real bridge games. But this example shows dramatically that there is much more to bridge than merely knowing good technique and percentage plays.

SOLUTION 39

North
- ♠ A
- ♡ A 10 8 6 3
- ◇ A Q 4 3
- ♣ Q J 6

West
- ♠ K 10 6 4 2
- ♡ K J 9 4 2
- ◇ —
- ♣ 8 5 4

East
- ♠ J 9 8 5
- ♡ Q 5
- ◇ J 8 7 6
- ♣ 7 3 2

South
- ♠ Q 7 3
- ♡ 7
- ◇ K 10 9 5 2
- ♣ A K 10 9

7◇ by South
Lead: ♣8

A crossruff is the only likely way home from this point, so you must plan to cash two more club tricks (two major-suit aces, one diamond, seven ruffs, and three clubs). Additionally, you must take care to avoid ending up with too many trumps in the closed hand — at the end, you must ruff with dummy's high trump, and have a simple tenace over East. This line will achieve your ends: spade ace, two more clubs, spade ruff, heart ace, heart ruff, spade ruff, heart ruff, club ruff with the diamond queen. If East turns up with four clubs, substitute a (safe) club ruff for the first spade ruff, and make the last (high) ruff in dummy a spade ruff.

North
- ♠ A K 8
- ♡ K 10 7 6
- ◇ Q J 9 3 2
- ♣ 2

West
- ♠ —
- ♡ J 9 5 4 2
- ◇ 10 6 5 4
- ♣ J 10 9 7

East
- ♠ 9 7 2
- ♡ Q 8
- ◇ A K 8 7
- ♣ A K 8 4

South
- ♠ Q J 10 6 5 4 3
- ♡ A 3
- ◇ —
- ♣ Q 6 5 3

4♠ by South
Lead: ♣J

Making your contract is not a problem, but at matchpoints the overtricks are important. Counting two clubs ruffs in dummy, you have eleven tricks. A twelfth will materialize if East's club king falls tripleton. Failing that, you may be able to produce a diamond trick after ruffing three times in the suit — you have three dummy entries available for this purpose (a trump at Trick 2, plus two club ruffs). If diamonds aren't going to bring in a trick by force, your best hope for a twelfth trick is a red-suit squeeze against West.

You can determine how best to play diamonds by using partial and inferential count information. For example, if West shows out at Trick 2 (see diagram), East is marked with three spades, two hearts, and, by hypothesis, at least four clubs. He has at most four diamonds, so you should go for the red-suit squeeze. This requires West to hold the diamond ten, and you must remove both of East's high honors to transfer the menace. The complete play would be: club ace, trump to North, low diamond ruffed (East might play the ten from ace-king-ten, or the king if he lacks the ten), club ruff, diamond queen covered and ruffed, club ruff, diamond jack covered and ruffed, trumps to squeeze West.

SOLUTION 41

North
- ♠ 10 6 4 2
- ♡ 3
- ◇ A K Q J 9
- ♣ 8 7 5

West
- ♠ 7
- ♡ Q J 10 9
- ◇ 10 8 7 4
- ♣ J 9 6 2

East
- ♠ Q J 8 5
- ♡ K 8 5 2
- ◇ 6
- ♣ Q 10 4 3

South
- ♠ A K 9 3
- ♡ A 7 6 4
- ◇ 5 3 2
- ♣ A K

6♠ by South
Lead: ♡ Q

You should win the opening lead with the ace of hearts, cash the ace of spades, and (assuming both opponents followed with small spades) continue with a small spade. If spades break 3-2, you regain the lead, draw the last trump and claim. If East shows up with four spades to the queen-jack, you win the club return, get to dummy with a heart ruff, pick up East's trumps, and claim. What you should not do is lead a diamond to North to play the second round of trumps from dummy (because if you finesse the nine of spades you expose yourself to a possible diamond ruff). Nor should you ruff a heart before leading the second round of trumps — if East has queen-jack fourth of spades he can split his honors, leaving you in a mess. If you duck, he can tap dummy with a heart. If you win, you cannot lead another trump because you have hearts to lose.

At matchpoints, you have the additional possibility of leading the first round of trumps from dummy, taking the double finesse, to make an overtrick if East started with queen-jack-small in spades. The possibility of the overtrick is too small for you to give up your best chance for the contract. West or East may have a singleton spade honor, and a 4-1 trump break may leave you awkwardly placed, depending on how you guess to handle your dummy entries. The key factor is that six spades is a very good contract to get to. Even if the overtrick were a good chance, you would be wiser to give yourself the best chance to make the contract.

North
- ♠ 6 5 3
- ♡ A K J 4
- ◊ J 7 5 2
- ♣ K 10

West
- ♠ 10 8 7
- ♡ 10 9 8 6
- ◊ 10 6
- ♣ 9 5 4 3

East
- ♠ Q 9 4 2
- ♡ 5
- ◊ Q 9 8 4
- ♣ 8 7 6 2

South
- ♠ A K J
- ♡ Q 7 3 2
- ◊ A K 3
- ♣ A Q J

6NT by South
Lead: ♡ 10

The best chance for three tricks in diamonds is to play ace, king and another. This picks up three diamond tricks when the suit is 3-3, or when either opponent has queen-singleton or queen-doubleton, or when West has four or more to the queen, for a total somewhere around 77%. Furthermore, you still make the contract when West's void or small singleton shows up on the first two rounds, if the spade finesse wins, for a grand total near 82%. This is clearly better than taking the spade finesse first, which has only queen-singleton or queen-doubleton of diamonds in reserve, and has an overall chance of under 60%.

A compromise play is probably best: play ace of diamonds, then a low diamond. This gives up the maximum chance in diamonds, since it loses to East's queen-doubleton. However, it keeps the spade finesse in reserve and makes the contract almost 70% of the time in diamonds, plus about half the rest of the time, and a small chance that East guards diamonds and West has the singleton or doubleton queen of spades, or more than 84%. Our arithmetic, which is notoriously poor, may be off a little, but whether the compromise attempt is slightly better or slightly worse than simply playing diamonds, we offer this advice if you adopt it: Do not play off one high spade in advance. If you do, East may win the second round of diamonds with the queen and play a spade. This will force you to decide whether or not to take the spade finesse before you have had a chance to test for a 3-3 diamond break.

SOLUTION 43

North
- ♠ K Q
- ♡ Q 8 7 4 2
- ◇ Q 6 4
- ♣ 8 4 3

West
- ♠ 10 9 7 6 2
- ♡ J 5
- ◇ 10 8 7 5
- ♣ Q 7

East
- ♠ J 5 4 3
- ♡ 9
- ◇ K 9 3
- ♣ 10 9 6 5 2

South
- ♠ A 8
- ♡ A K 10 6 3
- ◇ A J 2
- ♣ A K J

6♡ by South
Lead: ♠ 10

If your first finesse in the minors is the jack of clubs, you will make the contract when East has the queen of clubs, or when he has the king of diamonds singleton or doubleton. A better try is to strip the majors, and make your first minor-suit play a diamond to the jack. If this loses, you will need the club finesse (unless West's king of diamonds is a singleton). However, if the diamond jack holds you can continue with the ace-king-jack of clubs. This lands the contract when East has the queen of clubs, and adds the extra chance that West holds the club queen doubleton (or the club queen well guarded with a small singleton diamond). If the endplay fails to come off, you can still play East for the doubleton king of diamonds.

The fly in this ointment is that West may hold the king of diamonds yet not capture your jack. In principle, this possibility removes the advantage of starting diamonds first. We say more power to West if he finds that play.

SOLUTION 44

North
- ♠ 9 7 3
- ♡ K 6 3 2
- ◊ A 10
- ♣ A K Q 10

West
- ♠ A J 10 8 6
- ♡ 10 5
- ◊ J 9 8 7
- ♣ 4 2

East
- ♠ 5 4 2
- ♡ Q J 9 8
- ◊ 6 5 3
- ♣ 9 8 5

South
- ♠ K Q
- ♡ A 7 4
- ◊ K Q 4 2
- ♣ J 7 6 3

6♣ by South
Lead: ♠A

The main chances are a finesse of the ten of diamonds or a red-suit squeeze against East. You should plan the play so that you get as much information as possible about the opponents' distributions before deciding between them.

You should begin by cashing dummy's top clubs. If West turns up with a singleton club, the diamond finesse is more attractive than the squeeze. Ruff a spade, then lead a diamond to the ten. If East has a singleton club, the red-suit squeeze has better prospects than the diamond finesse. Ruff a spade, then finish the trumps.

If trumps break 3-2, the calculation is much closer. After the third round of trumps, ruff the last spade. Since West can be assumed, on the bidding, to have started with at least five spades, this ruff will provide a complete black-suit count. Your best continuation depends on that count.

(a) If West started with seven black cards, his six other cards must include a stopper in one red suit or the other. The squeeze has no chance. Finesse the ten of diamonds. (b) If West started with eight black cards, it is not clear without detailed calculations which line is better, so follow your intuition, or instincts, or hunch, or whatever it is you follow when you don't feel like doing all the arithmetic. (If you did the arithmetic, you would find out the squeeze is the better chance, but we don't think it pays to bother with big calculations to get very small advantages.) (c) If West started with nine black cards, your intuition or whatever should tell you that the squeeze is clearly the superior chance.

SOLUTION 45

North
- ♠ J 6 4
- ♡ A 3 2
- ◇ Q 10 7 6 5
- ♣ K 6

West
- ♠ 5
- ♡ K J 10 8 7 4
- ◇ 4 2
- ♣ J 9 7 5

East
- ♠ K 10 9
- ♡ Q 9 5
- ◇ A K 9 8
- ♣ Q 10 4

South
- ♠ A Q 8 7 3 2
- ♡ 6
- ◇ J 3
- ♣ A 8 3 2

4♠ by South
Lead: ◇ 4

The chances are good that East has a balanced hand, and very good that he has the king of spades. However, that still leaves a great many possibilities, quite a few different approaches declarer might adopt, and a wide variety of cases in which the different plays will win and lose.

Declarer can:

(a) Ruff with the ace, then lead a spade towards the jack (losing when West has singleton five, or any doubleton without the king — because East gets to threaten a second overruff);

(b) Ruff with the ace, enter dummy with a heart, and lead towards the queen of spades (losing when West has a singleton or tripleton spade, but succeeding when spades are 2-2);

(c) Ruff with the queen of spades, then cash the ace of spades (losing when West has a singleton spade);

(d) Ruff with the queen of spades, then lead towards the jack of spades (losing when East has king singleton or doubleton, or king-ten-nine);

(e) Ruff with the queen of spades, then later lead the jack (losing when West is long in spades — he won't overruff — or when he has either singleton king or singleton five);

(f) Ruff with the eight, planning to finesse the queen later (losing when West has the singleton ten or nine);

(g) Ruff with the eight, planning to run the jack later (losing when West has king-ten, king-nine, or three to the king).

Is that enough possibilities for you? It is for us. We'd go for line (g). We like two things about it: it picks up all singletons in the West hand, and it loses only when West has the king of spades, which seems unlikely on the bidding. West must have some pictures in hearts; if West also has the king of spades, that doesn't leave much for East's opening bid.

SOLUTION 46

North
- ♠ A Q J 2
- ♡ A K J 2
- ♢ A K Q 2
- ♣ 2

West
- ♠ 5 4
- ♡ Q 8 6 5
- ♢ 7 4 3
- ♣ J 10 9 8

East
- ♠ K 8 7 6
- ♡ 7 4
- ♢ J 10 6 5
- ♣ 7 4 3

South
- ♠ 10 9 3
- ♡ 10 9 3
- ♢ 9 8
- ♣ A K Q 6 5

6NT by South
Lead: ♣J

Here, again, there are many possible tries for declarer, but this time we're going to give only the one we like best — we think it is convincing. We think declarer should win the opening lead, cash a second high club discarding a diamond from dummy, and lead the heart ten to dummy's jack.

If the heart jack loses, declarer later uses the heart nine as an entry to cash the remaining high club (on which he discards the queen or jack of spades from dummy), then takes the spade finesse.

If the heart jack holds, declarer leads the spade queen and, if necessary, the spade jack from dummy, to try to force an entry to the closed hand, to pitch the heart deuce on the high club. When the spade king is singleton, doubleton, or tripleton, this will succeed. If the spade queen and jack hold, and the ace of spades does not bring in the suit, declarer tries hearts, then, if necessary, cashes dummy's diamonds, then guesses which defender can be thrown in with a major-suit card, forced to lead a club.

SOLUTION 47

North
- ♠ K 9 8 6 5 4
- ♡ Q 5 3
- ◇ 8 4 2
- ♣ 2

West
- ♠ 7 3
- ♡ 8 2
- ◇ A K J 10 9 6 5
- ♣ Q 4

East
- ♠ Q J 10
- ♡ K J 10 9 4
- ◇ Q 7
- ♣ 9 8 6

South
- ♠ A 2
- ♡ A 7 6
- ◇ 3
- ♣ A K J 10 7 5 3

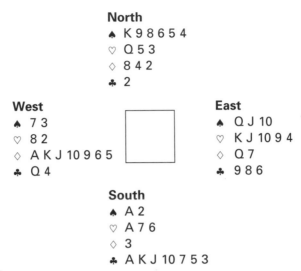

5♣ by South
Lead: ◇ K

Dummy's only sure entry is the king of spades. The question is how best to use it. Suppose you ruff at Trick 2, get to dummy with the king of spades, and take the club finesse. Even assuming you pick up clubs (which requires not only the queen onside but also a good split), you need to find West with the king of hearts (very unlikely on the bidding and early play), or to manipulate an endplay (a longshot).

You will probably be better off cashing the ace-king of clubs. If East drops the club queen, you can draw the last trump (even if East fooled you by falsecarding in clubs you still have a good chance), play ace, king and a third spade, pitching a heart if East has three spades, West two. (If West has the tripleton spade, you instead ruff and try to work an endplay against East.) If West drops the queen of clubs, you switch to spades, playing ace, king and another. Assuming spades are 3-2, you ruff, then throw East in by leading a low trump. At Trick 2, you should preserve the club three for this purpose. (If East ruffs the third spade from an original holding of two spades and three clubs, you discard a heart.)

If the queen of clubs doesn't fall, but clubs are 3-2, you switch to spades, intending to throw East in with a club after spades are established.

SOLUTION 48

North
- ♠ A 10 6 5 2
- ♡ A 6
- ◇ A 2
- ♣ A Q 6 5

West
- ♠ K J 8 7 4
- ♡ J 10 9
- ◇ 9 7 4
- ♣ 10 7

East
- ♠ Q 9
- ♡ Q 8 4 3
- ◇ 10 8 6 3
- ♣ 9 8 2

South
- ♠ 3
- ♡ K 7 5 2
- ◇ K Q J 5
- ♣ K J 4 3

7♣ by South
Lead: ♡ J

You need two ruffs in one major. Spade ruffs are safer than heart ruffs, since you will be ruffing on earlier rounds. So the basic line of play is heart king, spade ace, spade ruff low, heart ace, spade ruff, club king-jack, diamond ace, draw trumps, claim. Note that the heart ace, the more dangerous entry, is used before the diamond ace, because it is more likely an opponent could discard his last heart than his last diamond on the second spade ruff.

Can this basic line be improved? What about cashing some high trumps early to reduce the chance of a ruff? Clearly one high trump from the closed hand can be spared after the first spade ruff. What about cashing both the club king and jack at an early stage? This gains if West has two spades and two clubs, but it loses if East has two spades and three or four clubs, which is more likely. Therefore, it is not an improvement.

SOLUTION 49

North
- ♠ 4 3 2
- ♡ 7 6 5 2
- ◇ 9 4 3
- ♣ J 7 4

West
- ♠ 10 8 7 5
- ♡ 9 4 3
- ◇ Q J 6 2
- ♣ A K

East
- ♠ Q 9
- ♡ Q J 10
- ◇ K 8 7 5
- ♣ Q 8 5 3

South
- ♠ A K J 6
- ♡ A K 8
- ◇ A 10
- ♣ 10 9 6 2

1♣ by South
Lead: ♣A

You have an easy six tricks, but it takes imaginative play to land the seventh. Suppose you lead a trump. East can win, and continue diamonds. You will fend off the third round by pitching a heart; however, if you throw your low spade on the fourth round, good defense can arrange for West to win that trick, and give East a spade ruff. (Yes, you could have avoided the ruff by not cashing your top spades early, but that line would be inferior when the spade queen did not drop.) Leading the jack of spades fails — East will ruff, then draw dummy's last trump.

    You should plan to go for your spade ruff by leading your low spade. If East ruffs, your jack of spades (or a trump in exchange) will score. If West is allowed to win the spade trick, East cannot stop you from ruffing your winner in dummy. But watch out! East may be able to do something in hearts: he can discard a heart on the third round of spades, then another heart while you ruff your fourth spade in dummy. Now, you cannot get two heart tricks — unless you were careful to cash one high heart before leading your low spade. After you ruff the spade jack in dummy, you want to lead a second heart through East — if he ruffs, he will be ruffing a loser. (However, if West wins the third spade and leads a diamond, declarer should ruff and cash his second high heart before trumping the spade jack in dummy.) Note that you cannot afford to cash both high hearts, lest West win the third round of spades, then put East in with a heart to draw dummy's trump and force with a diamond. Cashing two hearts would succeed if East's distribution were 2-2-5-4, but that is less likely, as it would give West 4-4-3-2 with a heart honor — he might have doubled one club at favorable vulnerability.

The matchpoint swing is likely to be huge for plus 70 compared to minus 100. No contract is too small to be worthy of attention. This is probably as tough a one-club contract as you'll ever see.

SOLUTION 50

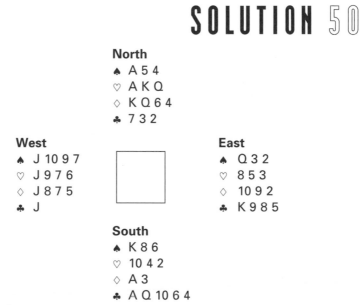

North
♠ A 5 4
♡ A K Q
♢ K Q 6 4
♣ 7 3 2

West
♠ J 10 9 7
♡ J 9 7 6
♢ J 8 7 5
♣ J

East
♠ Q 3 2
♡ 8 5 3
♢ 10 9 2
♣ K 9 8 5

South
♠ K 8 6
♡ 10 4 2
♢ A 3
♣ A Q 10 6 4

6NT by South
Lead: ♠J

A. You need four club tricks; your plan should be to take two finesses, hitting your target when the suit is 3-2 with East holding one or both of the missing honors.

Can you do anything about a 4-1 club split? Not if East has the singleton. When West has a low singleton club, you can finesse either the ten or the queen on the first round. The difference comes against singleton honors: finessing the ten first loses to singleton king or singleton jack; finessing the queen first loses to singleton king, but picks up singleton jack. Therefore, the best play is to lead a club to the queen. It's only a small difference, but no difference you can calculate is too small to be worthy of attention.

Cashing the club ace first would pick up both offside singleton honors, and also king-jack doubleton offside, which is a losing combination for finessing twice. However, it would lose to three cases of jack-small offside. (After cashing the ace, the ten-finesse would be best next, in case West started with a small singleton.)

B. In seven notrump, you need five club tricks; finesse the club ten.

SOLUTION 51

North
- ♠ Q 6 4
- ♡ J 9 4 3
- ◇ 8 6 5
- ♣ A J 4

West
- ♠ 5 2
- ♡ K Q 8
- ◇ J 9 7 4
- ♣ Q 10 8 2

East
- ♠ J 10 9 8 7 3
- ♡ A 7 2
- ◇ Q 10 3
- ♣ 9

South
- ♠ A K
- ♡ 10 6 5
- ◇ A K 2
- ♣ K 7 6 5 3

3NT by South
Lead: ♠5

The strongest approach is to maximize your chances of making four club tricks, as well as your three spades and two diamonds. (Good defense can probably stop any other attempt at nine tricks.) You should plan to lead to the jack of clubs at some point, to guard against West's holding four clubs to the queen.

The trap to avoid is trying to guard against too much. For example, suppose you win the first trick, cash the club king, and finesse the club jack. This wins, and you can now set up your nine tricks — but you can't take them. If you unblock spades and cash the spade queen before setting up clubs, the opponents will be able to cash hearts and spades when they get in with their club stopper. If you don't cash the spade queen, the opponents will take care to play only red suits later on, limiting you to eight tricks. Playing a club to the ace, a spade back, and a club towards dummy's jack, has similar defects. West can simply let the club jack win in dummy. Now, whether you cash the spade queen or not, you will go down.

The bottom line is that you have to pay off if East has the singleton queen of clubs. The correct play is to win the ace-king of spades, then immediately lead a club to dummy's jack. If that loses, you will need a 3-2 club break. If the club jack wins, you lead a low club from dummy, ducking if East shows out. Later, when you get to dummy with the club ace, you can safely cash the spade queen.

North
- ♠ A 8 6 2
- ♡ 7 6 2
- ◇ A 5 4 3
- ♣ K Q

West
- ♠ J 7 5 4
- ♡ J 10 9 8
- ◇ J
- ♣ 10 9 8 7

East
- ♠ K Q 10 3
- ♡ —
- ◇ Q 10 9 7 6
- ♣ 6 4 3 2

South
- ♠ 9
- ♡ A K Q 5 4 3
- ◇ K 8 2
- ♣ A J 5

6♡ by South
Lead: ♡ J

A. If West has 4-4-2-3 distribution, you can make the contract with a straightforward elopement, as follows: heart ace-king-queen, spade ace, spade ruff, club queen, spade ruff, club king, spade ruff, club ace, diamond king, diamond ace.

However, if you retain your trumps for control you can also succeed if West has 5-4-1-3 or 4-4-1-4. Just be careful not to let West discard on the second round of diamonds until you have finished all your black-suit business: heart ace, spade ace, spade ruff, club queen, club king, spade ruff, club ruff, spade ruff. Then the diamond king and a diamond towards the ace. If West's last card outside of trumps is a diamond (he was 4-4-2-3), he will follow suit — you are home. If he has a black-suit card, his choice is between discarding it, in which case the diamond ace is your twelfth trick, and ruffing your losing diamond . If he ruffs and returns a trump, you draw trumps; alternatively, if he ruffs and tries his black card, you ruff in dummy.

An alternative try, to duck the first trick and hope for an eventual diamond-spade squeeze, is inferior against strong defenders, for West may find a diamond shift, leaving only an unlikely trump squeeze for declarer.

B. No.

SOLUTION 53

North
- ♠ 5 3
- ♡ A Q 2
- ◇ A K 8 7 6 3
- ♣ K 6

West
- ♠ 2
- ♡ 9 8 7 5
- ◇ J 2
- ♣ Q 10 9 8 7 3

East
- ♠ Q J 9 8 4
- ♡ 6
- ◇ Q 10 9
- ♣ A J 4 2

South
- ♠ A K 10 7 6
- ♡ K J 10 4 3
- ◇ 5 4
- ♣ 5

6♡ by South
Lead: ♠2

On the bidding, it is virtually certain that East has the ace of clubs. It follows that there will be a shortage of winners if diamonds break 4-1. Assuming diamonds break favorably, there is a clear road to twelve tricks (indeed, thirteen tricks) when trumps are 3-2. To maximize your chances, you should try to guard against a 4-1 trump break. This can be done as follows: win Trick 1, heart jack, diamond ace-king and a third diamond ruffed with a high trump, heart to dummy.

Assuming diamonds are 3-2 but hearts 4-1 (see diagram), play another diamond from dummy, pitching the singleton club. The opponent with the long trump can ruff, but can do no damage.

SOLUTION 54

North
♠ 9 6 5
♡ K 10 4
◇ 8 7 3 2
♣ A Q J

West
♠ K Q J 8 7
♡ Q J 9 8 3
◇ K
♣ 6 4

East
♠ 10 4 3 2
♡ 7 6
◇ 10 9 6 5 4
♣ 3 2

South
♠ A
♡ A 5 2
◇ A Q J
♣ K 10 9 8 7 5

6♣ by South
Lead: ♠K

Your basic plan is to take the diamond finesse. However, since West's most likely distribution is 5-5-1-2, he may have the singleton king. You can take advantage of this chance whenever West has queen-jack of hearts, a lively possibility.

To set West up for the endplay, ruff dummy's last spade; then lead a heart, planning to insert dummy's ten. If this loses, use dummy's club and heart entries to take diamond finesses. But suppose West, with both heart honors, splits. You simply win dummy's king of hearts, and take a diamond finesse. If that finesse loses, West will be endplayed when he started with the expected 5-5-1-2.

SOLUTION 55

North
- ♠ 5 3
- ♡ A 7 4
- ◊ J 9 7 4 2
- ♣ Q 8 5

West
- ♠ Q J 9 8
- ♡ K Q J 9 3
- ◊ 10 8 6 3
- ♣ —

East
- ♠ 10 6
- ♡ 10 6 2
- ◊ 5
- ♣ A 10 9 6 4 3 2

South
- ♠ A K 7 4 2
- ♡ 8 5
- ◊ A K Q
- ♣ K J 7

3NT by South
Lead: ♡ K

It is possible for you to do something with spades without letting West on lead, but that is very unlikely. It is far more probable that East, who has shown up with three hearts, has no more hearts and at most two spades. If so, he can be forced to give dummy an entry to its diamond treasures.

You should throw a spade on the heart ace, then cash the spade and diamond tops. Next, so long as East had at least one diamond, lead the club seven to dummy's eight. When East's hand is similar to the one shown in the diagram, he will have no effective defense. If he lets dummy win the eight of clubs, you cash two diamonds for nine tricks. If East wins and plays the club ace, you unblock the club king; if East returns a lower club, you let it run to dummy's queen.

North
- ♠ K 10 8 3
- ♡ 7 5
- ◇ Q J
- ♣ A 9 6 4 2

West
- ♠ A 7 6 2
- ♡ K J 8
- ◇ 10 7 5
- ♣ 10 8 3

East
- ♠ Q 9 5
- ♡ Q 9 4 3 2
- ◇ 9 3 2
- ♣ 7 5

South
- ♠ J 4
- ♡ A 10 6
- ◇ A K 8 6 4
- ♣ K Q J

3NT by South
Lead: ♠2

You may have a theory as to which spade honor West is more likely to lead from. If so, act on it. We have no advice on that topic, but we do have some about how to play the suit if you decide to hope that West has the queen. Then, you should play the eight from dummy.

The purpose of this move is to simulate the play you would make with ace-doubleton in the closed hand. If your guess about the high spade honors is wrong and East in fact does hold the queen, he may go wrong by inserting the nine from queen-nine-small. Help him along as much as you can. If you play the three-spot from dummy, East's nine-play would be right only when declarer started with exactly ace-seven. Declarer's playing the eight would be entirely normal if his holding were ace-six or ace-four. East guesses.

Might the fact that East will sometimes go wrong with a queen-holding suggest that it is superior to guess that West has the queen rather than the ace?

SOLUTION 57

North
- ♠ Q 8 4 3
- ♡ 8 5 4 3
- ◇ 7 5
- ♣ K 5 3

West
- ♠ A K 7 6 5
- ♡ 9
- ◇ K 9 4 3
- ♣ A 8 6

East
- ♠ 10 2
- ♡ 6 2
- ◇ J 8 6 2
- ♣ J 10 9 7 4

South
- ♠ J 9
- ♡ A K Q J 10 7
- ◇ A Q 10
- ♣ Q 2

4♡ by South
Lead: ♠K

If East has the king of diamonds, you will eventually win a finesse in that suit to end up with ten tricks. If West has the king of diamonds, the bidding would be possible with either opponent holding the ace of clubs. However, you should assume West has the ace because dummy has too few entries for you to take advantage when East holds it.

You should overruff with an honor at Trick 3, draw trumps with tops from South, then lead the club deuce, putting up dummy's king if West plays low. Should East win this trick, you will be reduced to the diamond finesse. But when West has the ace of clubs you are home. If West ducks, you throw your remaining club on the good spade, then try the diamond finesse for an overtrick. If West puts up the club ace, dummy's blacks will provide two discards for your diamonds — you can get to dummy with a trump.

SOLUTION 58

North
- ♠ Q 8 4 3
- ♡ 10 8 5 4
- ◇ 7 5
- ♣ K 5 3

West
- ♠ K 7 6 5 2
- ♡ 9
- ◇ K 9 4 3 2
- ♣ J 9

East
- ♠ A 10
- ♡ 6 2
- ◇ J 8 6
- ♣ A 10 8 7 6 4

South
- ♠ J 9
- ♡ A K Q J 7 3
- ◇ A Q 10
- ♣ Q 2

4♡ by South
Lead: ♠5

This time dummy has two trump entries, so, if you wish, you may play East to hold the club ace. One trump entry can be used to lead a low club through East, the other to get back to dummy (either to reach the spade queen for a club discard when East ducks, or to reach the two black-suit discards when East hops up with his club ace). Alternatively, you could play West for the club ace, following the same procedure as in the previous problem.

It is better to play East for the ace. If East has the diamond king, you are going to make your contract whether you guess correctly in clubs or not. Therefore, assume that West holds the king (that is the only time your club guess matters). West is known to have five spades to the king, short hearts, and, by hypothesis, the king of diamonds. With the club ace as well, he might have overcalled, or doubled. So, play East for the ace of clubs.

You should overruff with a trump honor, draw two rounds of trumps ending in the North hand, and lead a low club.

SOLUTION 59

North
- ♠ Q J 10 9
- ♡ A 7 6 4 3
- ◇ 8
- ♣ 7 5 2

West
- ♠ A 2
- ♡ Q 9 5
- ◇ J 5
- ♣ Q 10 8 6 4 3

East
- ♠ 6 4
- ♡ K J 8 2
- ◇ Q 10 9 7 6
- ♣ J 9

South
- ♠ K 8 7 5 3
- ♡ 10
- ◇ A K 4 3 2
- ♣ A K

6♠ by South
Lead: ♠A

"Double squeezes are too difficult for me," we heard someone remark recently. This deal is a Christmas present for anyone who thinks that way. It's a double squeeze you 'know' is going to work, and you just can't help playing it correctly.

It is virtually impossible that West started with five diamonds, so if diamonds aren't established after two ruffs it will be East who guards them. Additionally, if West's bidding is anywhere near normal East won't be able to guard the third round of clubs. Your slam is as good as in the bag: spade at Trick 2, diamond ace-king, diamond ruff (to make it interesting, let's say East started with five or more diamonds), club king, diamond ruff, club ace, trumps, leaving (with South on lead):

- ♠ —
- ♡ A 7
- ◇ —
- ♣ 7

- ♠ 7
- ♡ 10
- ◇ 4
- ♣ —

You lead the last trump. West must keep a club to beat dummy's seven, so he can't keep two hearts. After West discards, throw dummy's club (assuming it is not good). East now can't keep both a diamond to beat the four-spot and two hearts. If your diamond isn't good, you will be able to win the last trick with the seven of hearts.

SOLUTION 60

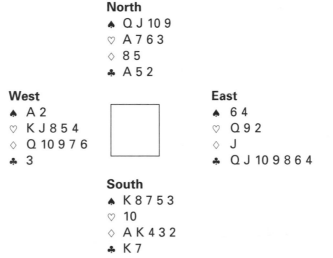

North
- ♠ Q J 10 9
- ♡ A 7 6 3
- ◇ 8 5
- ♣ A 5 2

West
- ♠ A 2
- ♡ K J 8 5 4
- ◇ Q 10 9 7 6
- ♣ 3

East
- ♠ 6 4
- ♡ Q 9 2
- ◇ J
- ♣ Q J 10 9 8 6 4

South
- ♠ K 8 7 5 3
- ♡ 10
- ◇ A K 4 3 2
- ♣ K 7

6♠ by South
Lead: ♠A

East isn't going to show up with five diamonds; if West has five, the only chances are a red-suit squeeze or a defensive miscue. You can play for both of those possibilities, after winning Trick 2, by playing ace, king and a third club, ruffing. In effect, you want to get one of your trumps played, to put pressure on West, without disturbing the entry position for the squeeze. (On a technical basis, you could equally well cash the ace-king of diamonds first. But why give the defense gratuitous information?)

After your club maneuver, play ace-king of diamonds. If two ruffs will make your last diamond good, continue diamonds; if not, attack hearts. When West started with at least five cards in each red suit (see diagram), he will have been squeezed by the third round of clubs.

SOLUTION 61

North
- ♠ 9 8
- ♡ Q J 10
- ◇ A K 5 3 2
- ♣ 7 6 4

West
- ♠ K 10 6 5 2
- ♡ 9 7 3
- ◇ Q 4
- ♣ 10 5 2

East
- ♠ A 4 3
- ♡ 8 6 5 4 2
- ◇ 8 7
- ♣ A 9 3

South
- ♠ Q J 7
- ♡ A K
- ◇ J 10 9 6
- ♣ K Q J 8

3NT by South
Lead: ♠5

If you thought that spades were 4-4, you could start by knocking out the ace of clubs. But you don't think so. Playing clubs could also work out satisfactorily if spades were six-two, with the club ace in the right hand for you — but in that layout you can equally well work on diamonds first.

Since spades appear to be five-three, your best chance is to hope to take five diamond tricks, unblocking hearts in the meantime to add three hearts and one spade, thus bringing your total to the desired nine. If entries were plentiful, the best percentage play for five diamond tricks would be to cash the ace and king, picking up the suit when the missing diamonds are 2-2, singleton queen, or void with East.

However, hearts is not the only suit needing to be unblocked. Diamonds are blocked also. Thus, the normal percentage play in the suit is much against the odds. For example, suppose you cash the ace-king of diamonds, and the suit splits 2-2. You still can't take nine fast tricks — even throwing a blocking diamond on a heart winner from dummy doesn't help. Under the circumstances, the best chance in diamonds is to run the jack immediately. This enables you to pick up the suit and to run five tricks any time West has the queen. Of course, you will cash the ace-king of hearts just prior to your use of dummy's last diamond honor. Note that it is inappropriate to cash one high diamond from dummy first. This works against singleton queen, but fails when diamonds are two–two.

North
- ♠ Q 9 4 3
- ♡ K 7
- ◇ J 10 6 5
- ♣ A 8 2

West
- ♠ J 10 2
- ♡ J 9 6 2
- ◇ 9 8 7
- ♣ 7 5 3

East
- ♠ 6
- ♡ A Q 8 5 4 3
- ◇ A K 4
- ♣ K Q 10

South
- ♠ A K 8 7 5
- ♡ 10
- ◇ Q 3 2
- ♣ J 9 6 4

3♠ by South
Lead: ♡2

There is no chance if trumps are 4-0, so assume otherwise. Then, your problem is to avoid two club losers. This requires either a spectacularly favorable lie in the suit, or an endplay.

In order to determine how best to play the clubs, you would like to find out the distribution of that suit, and, since it is necessary in some cases, you would also like to be in dummy at the point of decision. Therefore, you should ruff the heart at Trick 4, draw trumps, and finish the diamonds, throwing a club.

Barring exceptional circumstances, you should lead a low club from dummy. This gives up the chance that a sleepy East, with king- or queen-doubleton, would fail to unblock if you first cashed the ace, but it handles all other makable cases. If East plays a high honor, he is endplayed; if East plays the ten, you play him for honor-ten doubleton; if East plays low, you rise with the jack.

A tricky case (fortunately, quite unlikely to occur on this deal) arises if you determine that East has four clubs. You could play East for king-queen-fourth (6 cases), or for high-honor fourth (8 cases). The latter is more likely to have been dealt, but you may feel the former is more consistent with East's aggressive bidding and West's timidity.

SOLUTION 63

North
♠ 10 8 7 5 4 2
♡ 6
◇ Q 9
♣ A 10 9 4

West
♠ A K 9 3
♡ Q 10 8 7
◇ 6 5 4
♣ J 2

East
♠ Q 6
♡ A J 9 5 4 3 2
◇ 10
♣ Q 6 3

South
♠ J
♡ K
◇ A K J 8 7 3 2
♣ K 8 7 5

5◇ by South
Lead: ♠K

What's going on in spades? The only likely layout is that East started with
queen-doubleton. West, hoping East started with a small singleton spade,
was trying to cash the defense's second spade trick without handing
declarer extra tricks. Assuming the spade suit lies that way, you need
three entries to dummy in order to make use of spades — two for
ruffing, and one, presumably the ace of clubs (because using a trump
entry last would require a 2-2 split), to return and cash two winners.
Where will these entries come from?

One possibility is to finesse the nine of diamonds at Trick 3. If this
succeeds you are home: spade ruff, diamond queen, spade ruff, draw
trumps, club ace, claim. However, there is no hurry. You may as well ruff
the spade and exit with the king of hearts. Presumably East will win, and
he may do something that will help. A ruff-sluff or a trump play will
allow you to use dummy's nine of diamonds as an entry safely, without
risking finding East with the ten of diamonds. If East decides to lead a
club, you can use your judgment — if you wish, you can go for clubs, not
risking the diamond finesse; alternatively, you may judge that clubs won't
come in, in which case you can win the club king and lead a diamond to
the nine.

North
- ♠ Q 7 3
- ♡ A K 8 6 5
- ◇ J 4
- ♣ 10 9 2

West
- ♠ 9 8 5 4 2
- ♡ J 10 7
- ◇ A 6
- ♣ K Q 3

East
- ♠ —
- ♡ Q 9 2
- ◇ 9 8 7 2
- ♣ J 8 7 6 5 4

South
- ♠ A K J 10 6
- ♡ 4 3
- ◇ K Q 10 5 3
- ♣ A

6♠ by South
Lead: ♣K

You cannot afford to draw trumps, so the play is scheduled to develop as follows: you knock out the ace of diamonds, ruff the club return, and run diamonds. If West ruffs after dummy is out of diamonds, you overruff with the queen, draw trumps, and claim. What if West doesn't ruff? You will eventually run out of diamonds, and have to try to cash heart tricks. An intelligent West will throw his hearts on the diamonds, and you'll have to be very lucky to be able to cash the heart tricks at the end — you'll need a 7-2 club split.

Clearly it must be better to try to take the heart tricks you need earlier, before the last diamond (a closed-hand entry) is gone from dummy. How many heart tricks do you need?

A. Two, in the actual set-up. If West lets you run all the diamonds, you can get only three heart pitches from dummy — the ace king will still be there. So you should plan to cash the heart ace-king early, either immediately or after the first round of diamonds. This opens up the possibility of instant disaster. West may ruff, or East may have the diamond ace with four hearts and be able to give West an overruff in hearts. However, not cashing the high hearts is virtually suicidal against a competent West.

B. If dummy's distribution were 3-4-2-4, you need not risk playing both high hearts early. It would be sufficient to cash one of them. If, later on, West allows you to run all your diamonds, you throw hearts from dummy, including the remaining honor on the last round of diamonds. This creates a new heart loser in your hand, but you can fall back on an old method to take care of it — ruff it in dummy.

SOLUTION 65

North
- ♠ K 10 7
- ♡ A K 6
- ♢ A 6 4 3 2
- ♣ K 5

West
- ♠ J 5
- ♡ Q 10 7
- ♢ Q J 10 8
- ♣ 9 4 3 2

East
- ♠ 9 8 4 3
- ♡ 9 8 4 3
- ♢ K 9 7 5
- ♣ 7

South
- ♠ A Q 6 2
- ♡ J 5 2
- ♢ —
- ♣ A Q J 10 8 6

7♣ by South
Lead:♢ Q

It is not possible to take advantage of every possible way the contract could be made on a double-dummy basis. The best line of play is the one that combines the most likely chances. The ones you would most like to keep are: 3-3 spades, doubleton spade jack, 4-4 diamonds combined with 3-2 trumps, queen of hearts dropping singleton or doubleton, plus whatever squeezes might be available. Some of those potential squeezes have to go in order to retain the other possibilities.

You should begin by ruffing the opening lead in the closed hand (it is almost certain that, eventually, you will throw a heart on the ace of diamonds, but you would prefer to do it in a squeeze situation at the end, if possible, perhaps forcing East to keep the queen of hearts). Next, draw trumps, throwing a heart (and, if necessary, one or two diamonds) from dummy. If clubs break 3-2, a 4-4 diamond split will see you home, so enter dummy with a heart, ruff a second diamond, and test spades with the ace and king. This is necessary to take advantage of a doubleton jack of spades — the next diamond ruff is the last non-spade entry to the closed hand. If nothing exciting has happened, ruff a third diamond, then cash the ace-king of hearts, and try the ace of diamonds, planning to discard the heart jack if the heart queen has not yet appeared.

If clubs break 4-1, you cannot afford to ruff three diamonds, though you would still like to ruff two (for squeeze purposes — if diamonds are five-three, this will establish a diamond menace against one opponent, and may lead to a spade-diamond squeeze). Therefore, play the spade ace-king, ruff a diamond, then run the red-suit winners.

SOLUTION 66

North
- ♠ 6 4 2
- ♡ K J 10 6 2
- ◇ 9 7 4
- ♣ K J

West
- ♠ 9 7 5
- ♡ 5 3
- ◇ A 3
- ♣ 10 8 7 5 4 2

East
- ♠ K 10 8 3
- ♡ Q 9 8 7
- ◇ K 2
- ♣ 9 6 3

South
- ♠ A Q J
- ♡ A 4
- ◇ Q J 10 8 6 5
- ♣ A Q

3NT by South
Lead: ♣5

There is no time for diamonds, so you must hope for two spade tricks and five hearts, or three spades and four hearts. To give yourself the best shot at both possibilities, win the opening lead in dummy, and play a spade to the queen.

If this loses, you will need five heart tricks. Win the club continuation, cash your spades (might as well), then play ace and another heart, planning to finesse.

If the spade queen holds, assume that the finesse worked. True, a brilliant West, with the spade king and three hearts to the queen, might do you in by holding up in spades, but if he makes that play without tipping you off he deserves to come out on top. After winning the spade queen, play ace, king, jack of hearts, discarding the ace of clubs. Assuming this establishes hearts, the opponents cannot put you back in dummy without giving you nine tricks (including a second spade finesse); if they do anything else, you can go for diamonds. At worst, the defense will knock out a spade stopper. You switch to diamonds, and will be defeated only if an opponent who started with five or more spades has both high diamonds, which is unlikely.

SOLUTION 67

North
- ♠ A J 5 4 3
- ♡ K 7
- ◇ 10 8
- ♣ Q 9 6 2

West
- ♠ K 10 8 2
- ♡ —
- ◇ K J 7 3 2
- ♣ 8 7 5 3

East
- ♠ 9 7 6
- ♡ Q J 10 8
- ◇ Q 9 6 4
- ♣ A 4

South
- ♠ Q
- ♡ A 9 6 5 4 3 2
- ◇ A 5
- ♣ K J 10

4♡ by South
Lead: ◇ 3

Only a 4-0 trump break can cause a problem, and even then you may survive if you prepare for it. The key is to avoid using the king of hearts, dummy's only quick entry, prematurely. You should win the opening lead, and cash the heart ace. When hearts are not 4-0, you can lead to the heart king, making ten or eleven tricks depending on the trump split. (Or, you can think about whether it pays in the long run to play the queen of spades, intending to go up ace and ruff a spade if West does not cover. In theory this jeopardizes the contract — spade ruff, two minor-suit tricks, spade overruff — but to a tiny extent.)

When hearts do break 4-0, you will be where you want to be — in the closed hand, to take a spade finesse. And, just in case West ducks your queen of spades, you have the king of hearts where and when you need it, as a fast entry to let you throw your losing diamond on a spade winner.

North
- ♠ 10 8 6
- ♡ 7 5 4
- ◇ 9 8 6
- ♣ K Q J 7

West
- ♠ 4
- ♡ J 9 8 3
- ◇ Q 10 5 2
- ♣ A 6 5 4

East
- ♠ J 9 3
- ♡ Q 10
- ◇ J 7 4
- ♣ 10 9 8 3 2

South
- ♠ A K Q 7 5 2
- ♡ A K 6 2
- ◇ A K 3
- ♣ —

5♠ by South
Lead: ♣A

This is a good time to play carefully, because it would be painful — very painful — to hold the best hand you'll ever be dealt, get yourself up to five spades, have partner put down extra values in dummy, get a favorable lead, and then go down against routine distribution.

To avoid this fate worse than death, ruff the opening lead *high*, then lead the spade deuce, planning to cover whatever card West plays. You hope to take four spades, four red-suit tops, and three clubs (or the equivalent). Only a wildly unusual distribution will defeat this plan.

SOLUTION 69

North
- ♠ 10 9 5
- ♡ K 9 4
- ◇ 4 3
- ♣ A 10 9 5 3

West
- ♠ A Q J 6 4 2
- ♡ Q J 10 3
- ◇ —
- ♣ 8 7 4

East
- ♠ 8 3
- ♡ 8 7 6 5
- ◇ J 9 8 7 2
- ♣ J 2

South
- ♠ K 7
- ♡ A 2
- ◇ A K Q 10 6 5
- ♣ K Q 6

6NT by South
Lead: ♡ Q

Your original plan had been to run clubs, then make a decision about how to play the diamonds, based on the club count and on distributional inferences available from the bidding and the opening lead. As things stand, assuming clubs run you have eleven top tricks, but no safe way to establish a twelfth, so you must rely on some sort of useful end-position. Since it is impossible to rectify the count for a squeeze, you can do no better than run winners and hope that something develops.

After five clubs and two more diamonds, with a finesse, your hands will look like this:

North
- ♠ 10 9
- ♡ K 9
- ◇ —
- ♣ —

South
- ♠ K
- ♡ 2
- ◇ K 6
- ♣ —

If East can keep the protected ten of hearts (in addition to two diamonds), you cannot exert any pressure. Furthermore, it will be easy for East to defend correctly, abandoning spades, because he cannot expect his spades to be useful. So, assume that West started with all three heart honors — a strong possibility in view of the opening lead. Then, after you cash the king of diamonds, and West comes down to three cards, you can determine, hypothetically, whether dummy's hearts are going to be good. If they are, you pitch a spade from dummy and play hearts; otherwise, you throw a heart from dummy, lead the king of spades, and hope for the best. (You can be fooled out of a contract that could legitimately be made only when East started with doubleton-ten of hearts, which is very unlikely for many reasons.)

SOLUTION 70

North
- ♠ A 10
- ♡ 9 7 4 2
- ◇ K J 6 5
- ♣ 10 8 7

West
- ♠ 8 7 5
- ♡ Q J 10
- ◇ A 10 3
- ♣ J 6 4 3

East
- ♠ 9 6 4 3 2
- ♡ 8 6 5 3
- ◇ 8 7
- ♣ 9 2

South
- ♠ K Q J
- ♡ A K
- ◇ Q 9 4 2
- ♣ A K Q 5

6NT by South
Lead: ♡ Q

You would like to accomplish two things: (a) pick up diamonds with one loser whenever possible; (b) be able to take your winners ending in dummy, to take advantage of a possible heart-club squeeze against West. Unfortunately, (b) requires that the last winner be a diamond, so these objectives are incompatible. If you knew that diamonds were 3-2, you could continue that suit by playing an honor, or to an honor, in either hand, being careful only to throw the diamond nine under dummy's king. Later on, after cashing two high clubs (to test for doubleton jack while entries permit unblocking the club suit), plus the remaining heart and three spades, you would finish diamonds by leading the four-spot to a higher spot in dummy. This would enable you to take advantage of West's (or, conceivably, East's) holding the sole guard in both hearts and clubs (see diagram). However, if you make that move in diamonds you will forfeit a diamond trick when East started with ace-ten-eight-seven. The best way to take both possibilities into account is to lead the diamond king from dummy, intending to drop the nine under it if East plays the seven or ten. This can't lose anything, and may retain the squeeze possibility.

What if East takes the king of diamonds with the ace? Then you have to guess. East, perhaps accidentally, will have played a strong defense, regardless of his holding.

North

♠ A 4
♡ 10 7
♢ A J 10 9 6 4
♣ A K 3

West

♠ 10 6 3 2
♡ K Q J
♢ K 8 3 2
♣ 9 4

East

♠ J 9 8 5
♡ 9 6 5 2
♢ 5
♣ 10 8 6 2

South

♠ K Q 7
♡ A 8 4 3
♢ Q 7
♣ Q J 7 5

6NT by South
Lead: ♡ *K*

Ducking the first trick may save extra undertricks, but even at match-points that is unlikely to be a winning play. You are in an aggressive contract, and won't score much if it goes down. Meanwhile, ducking the first trick loses the contract in some cases when East holds the nine of hearts (see diagram).

After winning the first trick, you may as well run the queen of diamonds. If it loses, you will discover your fate immediately. If it wins, you would like to take out some insurance against a 4-1 diamond split; you should be willing to pay an overtrick as a premium, since making six notrump will give you most of the matchpoints anyway. Your plan is to run clubs and spades, pitching diamonds, before taking the diamond finesse again. Then, when you play a diamond to the jack, if that suit is 4-1 you can hope to throw West in with a heart for a diamond endplay. Of course, West may lack the jack of hearts and unblock his queen, but it's worth trying.

Note that you cannot squeeze West in some cases if you duck the first trick. In effect, this is because you allow an early second heart play, which will destroy the value of the ten of hearts. You might then have to play for a simple heart-diamond squeeze with the heart eight as a menace in the closed hand (you win the second heart, lead the queen of diamonds, then run the blacks). With the cards as shown, East's nine of hearts defeats that squeeze. Ducking the first trick could gain if East has exactly jack-doubleton of hearts and is void, or has a small singleton, in diamonds, a far less likely holding.

SOLUTION 72

North
- ♠ J 5 4 2
- ♡ Q 10 7
- ◇ 6
- ♣ A K 9 8 3

West
- ♠ K 10 9
- ♡ 9 5
- ◇ J 10 5 2
- ♣ J 7 6 2

East
- ♠ 7
- ♡ A K J 8 6 2
- ◇ 9 4 3
- ♣ Q 10 5

South
- ♠ A Q 8 6 3
- ♡ 4 3
- ◇ A K Q 8 7
- ♣ 4

4♠ by South
Lead: ♡ 9

Each of the possible ruffs — ace, queen, and eight — gains in specific cases, but these cases are by no means all equally likely. For example, ruffing with the eight comes out ahead if West started with the singleton seven (any other play loses). But this is very unlikely — for one thing, East might have opened one, not two, if he held the spade king (even more likely with king-ten-nine). Compared to ruffing with the queen, ruffing with the ace works if West's king of spades is singleton. That is certainly a possibility, but against that must be put the times West holds king-ten-nine, king-ten-seven, or king-nine-seven. In those instances, ruffing with the queen is the only successful play. Overall, playing the queen of spades at Trick 3 is best.

North
- ♠ Q 7 4 3
- ♡ J 8 6 2
- ◇ A 5
- ♣ K 10 9

West
- ♠ J 10 6
- ♡ K 9 7 5
- ◇ 10 7 4 2
- ♣ J 8

East
- ♠ A 9 8 2
- ♡ 10 3
- ◇ J 6
- ♣ Q 7 5 4 3

South
- ♠ K 5
- ♡ A Q 4
- ◇ K Q 9 8 3
- ♣ A 6 2

3NT by South
Lead: ♠J

The only danger to the contract is that you may have to lose the lead in both hearts and diamonds before you can cash nine tricks. The opponents may then be able to take three spades, one heart and one diamond. That can happen if West gets on lead for a fatal play through dummy's queen of spades.

Therefore, your plan should be to make it expensive for West to gain the lead, so expensive that it will cost the opponents their second red-suit entry. Accordingly, after winning the first trick with the king of spades you lead the four of hearts, intending to play dummy's jack. Should West win this trick with the king of hearts, you will have nine tricks to take; and there is no way for the opponents to take five. If West leads another spade, you withhold dummy's queen, but you play the queen on a third round of the suit.

If the heart jack holds, you can turn your attention to diamonds, needing only four tricks. Ace and another diamond, intending to finesse, is sure to work when East follows to the second round. When he shows out, you can go up with the diamond king, to pursue other chances.

Suppose the heart jack loses to the king, and East returns a heart. In this situation, you want to prevent West from gaining the lead in diamonds. You win the heart and lead the eight of diamonds, intending to pass it to East if West plays low. Unless West has four or more diamonds to the jack-ten, you can set up your nine tricks without letting him on lead.

SOLUTION 74

North
- ♠ J 9 3
- ♡ 10 5 3 2
- ◇ K Q 5 4 2
- ♣ 4

West
- ♠ A 10 8 7 6
- ♡ Q 6 4
- ◇ 7
- ♣ A 10 8 7

East
- ♠ 5
- ♡ J 9 8 7
- ◇ J 10 9 8
- ♣ K 5 3 2

South
- ♠ K Q 4 2
- ♡ A K
- ◇ A 6 3
- ♣ Q J 9 6

3NT by South
Lead: ♠ 7

You may have to lose the lead in diamonds as well as in spades. If so, the opponents may be able to get clubs going for three tricks, giving them a total of five. However, to win club tricks for themselves they have to give you one. You want to arrange that this club trick is your ninth trick, so that if the opponents switch to clubs you will not have to lose the lead a second time.

If you begin by clearing diamonds, East may get the lead to shift to clubs, setting up five tricks for the defense while West still has the ace of spades. It is safer for you to knock out the spade ace at once, leading the spade jack from dummy at Trick 2. If this holds, you can duck a diamond, guaranteeing nine tricks if the suit is not five-zero. (If you play ace and another diamond, ducking to East's four-card holding, East might think to play back a diamond; then, the South hand could be subject to a squeeze.)

Suppose West captures the jack of spades, and shifts to a heart. You win, play ace of diamonds, then (if no five-zero break) duck a diamond. If West instead shifts to clubs — say a club to East's honor and a club to your queen, ducked — you have nine tricks without the long diamond.

North
- ♠ K J 3
- ♡ A K J
- ♢ A K 7 2
- ♣ A J 3

West
- ♠ 6 5 2
- ♡ 6 4
- ♢ Q 10 6 5
- ♣ 10 8 7 4

East
- ♠ Q 9 8 7
- ♡ 10 9 5 3 2
- ♢ 9 8 4
- ♣ Q

South
- ♠ A 10 4
- ♡ Q 8 7
- ♢ J 3
- ♣ K 9 6 5 2

6NT by South
Lead: ♠2

At last a lucky lead! But do you deserve it? It depends what you played from dummy at Trick 1. If you didn't put in the jack, you may not enjoy your good fortune.

Playing the king from dummy fails to pick up three spade tricks when West led from the queen of spades. Playing the three from dummy is even worse. The chances are very good that East has the queen of spades and will play it, driving out the ace from the closed hand. This leaves only one entry back to the South hand, the queen of hearts. Thus, you could not afford the safety play in clubs — ace of clubs, back to the South hand, then a club towards the jack. This requires a late South re-entry, in case West has four clubs to the queen-ten. The best you could do, under the circumstances, would be to win the spade ace and lead a club to dummy's jack, which picks up all 4-1 club splits with one loser except singleton queen with East.

To be sure, it would be very unlucky for East to have been dealt the singleton queen of clubs, but if you were stung by that particular piece of bad luck, you'd deserve it.

SOLUTION 76

North
- ♠ K J 10
- ♡ 8 7 6 2
- ◇ A
- ♣ Q 9 5 4 2

West
- ♠ 8
- ♡ A K Q J 9 5 4
- ◇ 10 7 4 3 2
- ♣ —

East
- ♠ 6 4 3
- ♡ 10 3
- ◇ Q J 9 6
- ♣ A 10 8 7

South
- ♠ A Q 9 7 5 2
- ♡ —
- ◇ K 8 5
- ♣ K J 6 3

6♠ by South
Lead: ♡ 4

The opening lead may seem like bad news, a virtual guarantee that West is void of clubs. The good news is that you can use this information to squeeze-endplay East into helping you in clubs.

You should ruff at Trick 1, lead a spade to dummy, ruff a heart, and lead another spade to dummy. Suppose trumps are 2-2. You can ruff a heart, lead a diamond to the ace, and ruff the last heart. At this point, your hands look like this:

North
- ♠ K
- ♡ —
- ◇ —
- ♣ Q 9 5 4 2

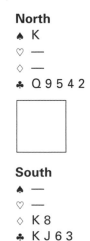

South
- ♠ —
- ♡ —
- ◇ K 8
- ♣ K J 6 3

If East has thrown a club, you can knock out the club ace and claim.

If East has not thrown a club (so that he has four clubs and two diamonds at this stage), you play diamond king, diamond ruff, club to the king, club to the queen.

Suppose now that East turns up with three trumps (see original diagram). When you discover this upon leading the second trump to dummy, you cash the ace of diamonds, then lead a third round of hearts from dummy to squeeze East in this position:

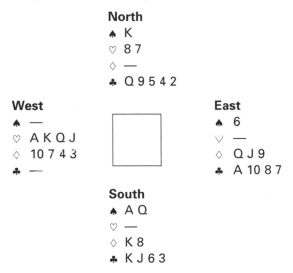

North
♠ K
♡ 8 7
◊ —
♣ Q 9 5 4 2

West
♠ —
♡ A K Q J
◊ 10 7 4 3
♣ —

East
♠ 6
♡ —
◊ Q J 9
♣ A 10 8 7

South
♠ A Q
♡ —
◊ K 8
♣ K J 6 3

East cannot afford to throw a club — you would draw his trump and attack clubs. If he throws a diamond, you will ruff the heart, cash the king of diamonds, ruff a diamond, lead a club to the king, draw the last trump, and lead a club to the queen. East makes it hardest for you by ruffing the heart, but you can counter by overruffing, ruffing your low diamond in dummy, and then squeezing East by leading a club to the king and your last trump, or, perhaps more stylishly, simply ruffing another of dummy's hearts.

SOLUTION 77

North
♠ A J 9 8 7 6
♡ Q J
♢ A J 9
♣ A 2

West
♠ Q 10 3
♡ 10 7 5 3 2
♢ 8 7 5
♣ 10 9

East
♠ 2
♡ 9 8 6 4
♢ Q 6 4 3 2
♣ 8 7 4

South
♠ K 5 4
♡ A K
♢ K 10
♣ K Q J 6 5 3

7NT by South
Lead: ♣ 10

If East is about to show out at Trick 1, you will try to pick up spades. In view of the five-zero club split, it will be more likely that West was dealt singleton ten than queen-ten doubleton. Therefore, your first spade play will be dummy's ace, intending to finesse if West plays the ten.

If East does not show out at Trick 1, you will have twelve top tricks, needing one more from spades or diamonds. You could gather what information is available and use it to play spades to best advantage, but it is much better to give yourself a chance at both suits. (The club information would change your normal play in spades only when West led a singleton ten of clubs.) You can test spades, getting your extra trick from a 2-2 split, singleton queen, or void with East (by playing the king first); then, if necessary, you take your best shot in diamonds. However, if you play enough clubs to be sure of the distribution of that suit, you will destroy the last entry back to the North hand; this will lose the option of finessing diamonds through East, which is the option you will probably want to elect if West turns up with long spades.

Therefore, you should win the first trick in the closed hand; then, assuming clubs are not 5-0, try the king and ace of spades; then, if spades have not come in, play the hand short in spades for the queen of diamonds.

North
- ♠ K 10 7 6
- ♡ A 6 5
- ◇ 7 2
- ♣ A 6 4 3

West
- ♠ 5 3 2
- ♡ 7
- ◇ A Q 9 8 6 4
- ♣ K J 10

East
- ♠ Q J 9 8
- ♡ J 9 8 3
- ◇ 5
- ♣ 9 8 7 2

South
- ♠ A 4
- ♡ K Q 10 4 2
- ◇ K J 10 3
- ♣ Q 5

4♡ by South
Lead: ♠2

East probably has one or both of the missing spade honors, so West, for his overcall, will surely have ace-queen of diamonds and the king of clubs. Therefore, trying to get an extra trick by leading up to the queen of clubs is a lost cause, and it is almost certain that trying for a diamond ruff in dummy will be unsuccessful.

However, there is an attractive alternative. With West marked with the minor-suit strength, you can draw trumps, eliminate West's spades when convenient, and attack diamonds. Eventually, you can throw West in with a diamond and force him to lead away from the king of clubs.

For example, with the typical lie of the cards as shown in the diagram, you can win the opening lead with the spade ace, draw trumps while preserving dummy's side-suit entries (heart king, then heart ace), and play the king of diamonds, intending to continue high diamonds until you take a diamond trick. If at any point West wins a diamond and plays a spade, you take dummy's king of spades, then ruff a spade to complete the strip. In fact, you can do this yourself at any convenient time prior to throwing West in. There will be no problem about the minor-suit count, since East will show out on an early round of diamonds.

SOLUTION 79

North
♠ A J 6 3
♡ K 5 4
◇ Q 9 2
♣ 10 8 7

West
♠ 2
♡ 7 6
◇ K 10 6 4 3
♣ J 6 5 4 2

East
♠ K Q 10 8 5
♡ 3 2
◇ A 8 7 5
♣ Q 9

South
♠ 9 7 4
♡ A Q J 10 9 8
◇ J
♣ A K 3

4♡ by South
Lead: ♠2

The opening lead is annoying because it forces you to use dummy's only side-suit entry before you can do any preliminary work. You cannot afford to duck the first trick, because the opponents could take a spade, a spade ruff, a diamond and a second spade ruff.

All is not yet lost, however. In addition to the outside chance that the queen-jack of clubs will drop doubleton, you may be able to work an elimination against East. This will depend on East's holding at most two clubs; also, it may require a 2-2 trump split, since you need dummy's king of hearts as a late reentry. To execute this plan, you should draw two rounds of trumps with the queen and jack. If trumps are 2-2, cash the ace-king of clubs and exit with the jack of diamonds.

Your hope is that East is out of clubs. If so, he is endplayed if he wins this trick. (Should East win and return a low diamond, you discard a spade.) Indeed, East may well be forced to win the trick, since he is likely to have ace-king of diamonds for his opening bid. However, even if West can and does win the diamond (see diagram), you still have a chance. West can cash a club but then must lead a diamond; you will play him for the ten of diamonds.

If East has a singleton trump, you need some help from the defense. Your best chance is probably to leave West with a trump, cash the ace-king of clubs, and lead the jack of diamonds, hoping that East has ace-king of diamonds and doesn't find the winning defense of playing spades, allowing West to ruff and cash a club.

North
- ♠ J 8 7 2
- ♡ Q 4
- ◇ A Q 9 6
- ♣ 8 4 3

West
- ♠ A 10 5
- ♡ 10 9 8 6
- ◇ 7 5 4 3 2
- ♣ J

East
- ♠ K Q 9 6 4
- ♡ J 7 5 3 2
- ◇ 8
- ♣ A 10

South
- ♠ 3
- ♡ A K
- ◇ K J 10
- ♣ K Q 9 7 6 5 2

5♣ by South
Lead: ♡ 10

If West has all three trumps, you won't find out about it in time to take advantage of a favorable diamond distribution. If East has all three, you can neutralize the potential second defensive trump trick by leading clubs twice from dummy. Therefore, your main plan should be to lead a diamond to dummy, then a club towards the closed hand, prepared to repeat the procedure should East show up with all the missing trumps.

However, to do that courts a new danger — the opponents may be able to get a diamond ruff. Since that ruff requires a 5-1 diamond break plus other conditions, it is worthwhile to risk it in exchange for picking up the 3-0 trump break. But you can minimize the chance of the diamond ruff by leading a spade at Trick 2. This will prevent East-West from getting a diamond ruff when the trump ace is in the hand with the singleton diamond (see diagram), because they will have no entry to give the ruff.

The spade play also courts new dangers — for example, West might have a singleton spade; or East might have two black-suit singletons — but they are so unlikely compared to the possibility of a diamond ruff that they may safely be ignored.

SOLUTION 81

North
- ♠ K J 9 8 3 2
- ♡ A
- ◇ Q 10 7
- ♣ 7 6 5

West
- ♠ Q 5
- ♡ Q 10 7 5 3
- ◇ 4 2
- ♣ 10 8 4 2

East
- ♠ A 10 7 6 4
- ♡ J 9 8
- ◇ 6 3
- ♣ K J 9

South
- ♠ —
- ♡ K 6 4 2
- ◇ A K J 9 8 5
- ♣ A Q 3

6◇ by South
Lead: ◇2

Line One: Win the lead, heart ace, club finesse, take two ruffs in dummy. For success, this requires the club finesse onside and clubs not six-one.

Line Two: Use dummy's four red-suit entries to take three ruffing finesses in spades, intending to set up and run that suit. Of the three finesses, two or three will win half the time (roughly, there are eight distributions of the missing spade honors, half of which find East with more honors than West), but beyond that you also need a 4-3 spade split or some combined luck — a trump break, the club finesse. This is not as good as Line One, where the luck needed beyond the fifty-fifty chance is less.

Line Three: Play on spades as in Line Two, but, instead of taking finesses, try for ace-tripleton of spades. If the opponents always played perfectly, this would not be as good as Lines One or Two, since the ace-tripleton of spades is less than a fifty-fifty chance even when spades break 4-3. However, East might play the spade ace from ace-fourth (and there would be chances if he played it from ace-doubleton or ace-fifth).

What play is best? The best general plan is probably a combination of Lines One and Three. Intend to rely on the club finesse, but first give East a chance to play his spade ace prematurely. Win the trump lead in dummy and play a low spade. If nothing interesting happens, ruff, play a heart to dummy's ace, and proceed with Line One. If East plays the spade ace, you have your contract without a finesse. If East plays the spade queen — unlikely, since declarer's play would be unreasonable with a singleton ten — you might well decide that a variation of Line

Two is indicated. In any case, this is a situation in which human actions are likely to count for more than a few percentage points of technical chance. Your spade void was not indicated by the bidding.

Assuming fully human opponents, this might be the best line: Win the opening lead in dummy and lead the eight of spades. This gives East his chance to err by playing the ace. If East plays low, let the eight ride. If it holds, or loses to the ace, you may have solved all your problems. If the eight loses to the queen, continue taking spade finesses. If the eight loses to the ten, try for the ace-tripleton of spades. To be sure, an opponent with queen-ten or ace-queen could mess up this plan by playing the "wrong" honor at the right time — but few opponents will actually do that.

SOLUTION 82

North
- ♠ Q J 4 2
- ♡ K 6 4
- ◇ 10 9 4 3
- ♣ Q 3

West
- ♠ K 5
- ♡ J 10 8
- ◇ K 7
- ♣ A K J 9 7 2

East
- ♠ 8
- ♡ Q 9 7 5 3
- ◇ J 8 6 5 2
- ♣ 8 5

South
- ♠ A 10 9 7 6 3
- ♡ A 2
- ◇ A Q
- ♣ 10 6 4

4♠ by South
Lead: ♣K

West probably has one or both side-suit kings for his overcall — East won't show up with both. When East has the king of diamonds, you will wind up making the contract whatever you do. If East has the spade king, West's defense was horrible, since he had you down merely by continuing with two more rounds of clubs, a routine play. So, you should gear your planning to the case in which West has both pointed-suit kings.

Now West's defense makes sense. He fears playing two more rounds of clubs, forcing you to ruff in dummy, because this will reveal his king of spades (which may be singleton). And he has set a trap for you. Suppose that you deduce that West has the king of spades; so, after winning the heart shift, you cash the ace of spades, hoping to drop West's singleton king. What drops is your contract, now unmakable. West has a safe club exit, and cannot be endplayed.

If the king of spades is singleton now it will still be singleton later. The correct play is to win the heart ace and lead a club. Your plan (on a club continuation) should be to ruff your club loser (high) in dummy, then cash the ace of spades, then (if the spade king remains at large) eliminate hearts, and finally throw West in with the king of spades, forcing him to lead diamonds or concede a ruff-sluff.

North
- ♠ Q 3
- ♡ A Q
- ◇ 9 7 5 4 3 2
- ♣ A K 8

West
- ♠ A K 7
- ♡ 10 6 5 2
- ◇ Q J 8
- ♣ 9 4 3

East
- ♠ J 8
- ♡ K 9 7 4
- ◇ 10 6
- ♣ J 10 6 5 2

South
- ♠ 10 9 6 5 4 2
- ♡ J 8 3
- ◇ A K
- ♣ Q 7

4♠ by South
Lead: ♡2

You must contrive not to lose three trump tricks despite your tenuous holdings. There are only a few combinations of the missing cards where this is possible with any play. Still, the idea is to do the best you can whether you are a favorite or an underdog. At least there are only a few situations to think about: when West holds (1) ace-king-small, (2) high honor-jack, and (3) jack-small. Leading low to the queen wins against (1) and (2) but loses to (3). Leading the ten, intending to run it, wins against (3) but loses to (1) and (2). So far, no contest. But what about a combination attempt? Suppose you lead the ten, intending to go up queen if West plays the seven or eight. Does this not give West the opportunity of making the mistake of covering from jack-eight or jack-seven? In a way, yes. But suppose West does cover the ten with the jack, and it goes queen, honor. On the next lead from dummy, East plays the eight or seven. What now? You cannot pick up both (2) and (3). Therefore, in theory this play can never be better than always leading to dummy's queen. If you think you can guess what West is doing when he plays the jack, you can come out ahead. If you don't guess as well as you think, you'll come out behind.

SOLUTION 84

North
- ♠ K 7 6
- ♡ 7 6 5 3
- ◇ J
- ♣ A K Q 8 4

West
- ♠ A J 9 8
- ♡ 4 2
- ◇ K 7 6 5 4 3
- ♣ J

East
- ♠ 5 3
- ♡ 9
- ◇ Q 10 9 8 2
- ♣ 10 7 6 5 2

South
- ♠ Q 10 4 2
- ♡ A K Q J 10 8
- ◇ A
- ♣ 9 3

6♡ by South
Lead: ♡2

Your basic plan is to draw trumps, then attack clubs. When clubs are 3-3, you are home free; if 4-2, as they would be in real life, the extra club trick you establish is your twelfth if you can get to it: you ruff the fourth round of clubs, cash ace of diamonds, then lead to the spade king hopefully. However, when clubs are 5-1 or 6-0, as they will always be in a declarer-play quiz, you will need to rely on spades for an extra trick. How will you play the spades? If West is the opponent who is very long in clubs, so that East figures to be longer in spades, you will want to take the normal spade play — a spade to the king, a spade back to the ten.

In contrast, when East is the opponent very long in clubs, the problem is more complicated. Suppose spades are 3-3: the normal play would still be best. Suppose West has four or more spades: it is superior to attack spades by leading a spade to the queen in an elimination position. If West wins, you hope he will have to lead away from the spade jack; if your spade queen wins, play back to the spade king. This loses only when East started with jack-small (4 cases), whereas the normal spade play loses when East started with ace-small (4 cases) or two small (6 cases), as well a small singleton. (Also, should the 4-2 spade split be likely but not certain, the "funny" spade play gains against some of the 3-3 splits, although it loses to more of them.) If East had five or six clubs, he is unlikely to have as many as three spades, because that would give him at most four diamonds, giving West at least seven diamonds.

Therefore, you should win the first trick, draw the remaining trump, and cash the ace of diamonds before starting clubs.

(a) If both defenders follow twice in clubs, cash the club queen discarding a spade. Then, if necessary, ruff the fourth round of clubs. When clubs are 4-2, continue by leading to the spade king except when East has shown up with four clubs and two hearts, in which case play the spade queen from the closed hand before leading to the spade king.

(b) When West has a singleton club honor, leave the club queen in dummy and lead a spade to the queen.

(c) When West has a low singleton club or a club void, play spades by leading up to the queen, as in (b).

(d) When East has a low singleton club or a club void, play spades by leading to the king, finessing the ten later if necessary.

SOLUTION 85

North
- ♠ Q 7
- ♡ K 9 6
- ◇ J 10 8 7 4
- ♣ J 7 5

West
- ♠ K 6 4 3
- ♡ A Q 7 3
- ◇ K 9 3
- ♣ 9 4

East
- ♠ J 9 5 2
- ♡ J 5 2
- ◇ 6 2
- ♣ 10 8 6 3

South
- ♠ A 10 8
- ♡ 10 8 4
- ◇ A Q 5
- ♣ A K Q 2

3NT by South
Lead: ♡ 3

If hearts were the only consideration, you could afford to duck the first trick, intending to go up with dummy's king on the next round of the suit. On the bidding, West is likely to hold the heart ace, but the first-round duck guards against the possibility that he has the queen-jack in a light takeout double.

However, there is a much greater danger lurking. If you duck the first trick, East may shift to spades. You would have to duck that, lest the entire spade suit be open. And West might win the spade king, then clear hearts before you have nine tricks to take. So, you should go up with dummy's heart king, and attack diamonds. The contract will very likely go down when hearts are 5-2, but ducking the first trick won't help you in that set-up.

SOLUTION 86

North
♠ 8 4
♡ K 10 6
◇ J 3
♣ A Q 9 7 5 2

West
♠ A J 7 3
♡ 9 8 7
◇ 10 4
♣ J 8 6 4

East
♠ Q 6 5 2
♡ 5 4 3 2
◇ 8 7 5 2
♣ 3

South
♠ K 10 9
♡ A Q J
◇ A K Q 9 6
♣ K 10

6NT by South
Lead: ♡9

There is no problem if clubs run. What if they don't? It seems right to run diamonds, to put an opponent with a club guard under pressure. (You cannot conveniently guard against the very unlikely occurrence that one opponent stops both diamonds and clubs; but just in case someone is going to show out on the first diamond, win the first heart in the closed hand.) Assuming diamonds run, you cash the club king-ace; when clubs don't break, run the red suits, leaving:

North
♠ 8
♡ —
◇ —
♣ Q 9

South
♠ K 10 9
♡ —
◇ —
♣ —

(a) If East has the club guard, and a long heart is outstanding, your only chance is to lead a spade and to hope that East has left himself with the ace, or that he held the long heart and the queen-jack of spades. If the long heart has been discarded, you still lead the spade from dummy, but this time you will prevail if East has left himself with the singleton ace or queen of spades; also, perhaps, if East has been squeezed out of a spade honor.

(b) If West has the club guard, and there is a heart of unknown location outstanding, you lead a spade from dummy in hope that West will be forced on lead. (If West has the heart, and East the ace-queen-jack of spades, so that you could have made the contract by cashing another club, that's too bad.) It could also work best to cash the high club when there is no heart outstanding, but it is against the odds, especially against decent defenders. In the last case, if you lead a spade from dummy and East plays the last remaining small spade, do not play your king — you very much do not want to win that trick.

SOLUTION 87

North
- ♠ A Q 6
- ♡ K 8
- ♢ J 10 9
- ♣ 7 5 4 3 2

West
- ♠ J 10 9 7
- ♡ J 10 9 7 6
- ♢ 8 5
- ♣ Q 10

East
- ♠ 3 2
- ♡ Q 5 4 2
- ♢ A 7 4 3 2
- ♣ K J

South
- ♠ K 8 5 4
- ♡ A 3
- ♢ K Q 6
- ♣ A 9 8 6

3NT by South
Lead: ♡ J

Time is short, so you can't set up tricks both in clubs and diamonds. It will be right to go after diamonds if two extra tricks are enough; otherwise, you will need to depend on a 2-2 club break.

To find out which minor to attack, win the first trick and start spades. If spades are worth four tricks, switch to diamonds for two tricks. If spades are worth only three tricks, switch to clubs (being careful to unblock) and hope for four tricks there.

A mid-course adjustment must be considered if West drops two high cards (from among the jack, ten and nine) when you cash dummy's ace-queen of spades. The chance that these plays are from two doubleton honors is almost three times as great as that they are from jack-ten-nine tripleton; since a 2-2 club split (with the extra chance of 3-3 spades) is a worse chance than that of gaining the needed trick in spades, you should plan to finesse the spade eight. You should execute that plan right away, leading the third spade from dummy immediately, intending to finesse the eight. That is, you should not switch to diamonds at that point. If you do, you may find that West has fooled you without risk (see diagram).

North
- ♠ 9 6 5
- ♡ A J
- ◇ K Q 10 8
- ♣ 10 9 8 3

West
- ♠ 8
- ♡ K 7 6 4 3
- ◇ J 7 6 4
- ♣ K 7 4

East
- ♠ A 7 4
- ♡ 10 9 8 2
- ◇ 9 3 2
- ♣ J 5 2

South
- ♠ K Q J 10 3 2
- ♡ Q 5
- ◇ A 5
- ♣ A Q 6

6♠ by South
Lead: ♡4

If you refuse the heart finesse, you will have to take a pitch on the diamonds before starting trumps. However, since you have no sure trump entry to dummy you will need to take the double club finesse right away — the circumstances that would allow you to profit from a tripleton jack of diamonds are less likely than a successful second club finesse. The play would have to go: heart ace, club ten winning (or covered and won), three diamonds to pitch a heart, club finesse, trumps. You would not need the heart finesse, but you would need two club finesses, a good break in diamonds, and something further (since there is the threat of a third-round club ruff when the opponents win the ace of trumps).

The heart finesse is a better chance, because if that succeeds you become a favorite. You win the heart jack in dummy, and attack trumps. If West has the spade ace, you will have a chance to test diamonds, then fall back on the club finesse; or, you can play for a diamond-club squeeze, which is almost as good. If East wins the spade ace, and reduces your options by shifting to a club, you can play for the minor-suit squeeze.

SOLUTION 89

North
- ♠ 7 4 3
- ♡ A 10 9 7 6 4 2
- ◇ —
- ♣ A Q J

West
- ♠ J 5 2
- ♡ 5
- ◇ Q J 10 9 6 4 3
- ♣ 6 5

East
- ♠ K Q 10 8
- ♡ Q J 8
- ◇ 8 7 5
- ♣ 4 3 2

South
- ♠ A 9 6
- ♡ K 3
- ◇ A K 2
- ♣ K 10 9 8 7

7♣ by South
Lead: ◇ Q

The entry position makes it very unlikely that playing for three ruffs in dummy will succeed. However, the chance of a 2-2 heart break can sensibly be combined either with two dummy ruffs plus a squeeze, or with a heart ruff to establish the suit after an incomplete trump removal. Which of these is the better chance?

Line One: Diamond ace-king (throwing spades), diamond ruff, spade ace, spade ruff high, trumps. Assuming no outrageous breaks, this line works when East guards hearts and West has either no spade honor or fewer than three spades.

Line Two: Diamond ace, two top clubs. If clubs are not 3-2, draw trumps (a ruff may be interpolated) and hope for 2-2 hearts. When clubs are 3-2, continue with heart king, heart ace, heart ruff, trump to dummy. With East guarding hearts, this succeeds when West has two clubs.

To compare the two lines roughly, assume a situation in which West has exactly seven diamonds and one heart. Ignoring eight-five-deuce of spades in West, Line One succeeds when West has two spades and three clubs, or one spade and four clubs, while Line Two works when West has three spades and two clubs. The winning cases for Line One split the black suits 2-5 and 3-2, or 1-6 and 4-1; the winning case for Line Two splits the black suits 3-4 and 2-3. The Line Two case is more balanced, thus significantly more likely than the main Line One case; the chance of West's having 1-1-7-4 is slim in comparison.*

*For those who like actual numbers, there are 245 ways West can have 2-3 or 1-4 in the blacks (210 2-3s plus 35 1-4s), and 350 ways he can have 3-2 in the blacks. Both the informal and formal calculations suggest that Line Two is superior. It is the best line overall.

SOLUTION 90

North
- ♠ 6 2
- ♡ 8 7 5 3
- ◇ A J 10 9 4
- ♣ 10 2

West
- ♠ Q 9 7 3
- ♡ 6 4 2
- ◇ Q 8 7 3 2
- ♣ 8

East
- ♠ A K 8
- ♡ K 10 9
- ◇ 5
- ♣ Q 7 6 5 4 3

South
- ♠ J 10 5 4
- ♡ A Q J
- ◇ K 6
- ♣ A K J 9

3NT by South
Lead: ♣8

You might as well start by playing the club ten from dummy. If East lets that hold, you can continue with a heart or club finesse. More likely East will cover with his queen, putting you in the closed hand.

It would be too risky to play king and another diamond, finessing. Diamond king-ace would ensure two diamond tricks and a dummy entry for a major-suit lead, which would be good enough for eight tricks if the heart finesse wins, but might not be good enough for nine.

A better shot at nine tricks is to start with a low diamond to dummy's nine. If East wins, you have nine tricks (you might need a heart finesse), and will go down only if the opponents can take four quick spade tricks (which requires West to have two honors). If the diamond nine holds, either because West has the diamond queen or because East is holding up to prevent your running the suit, you can take the opportunity to finesse in hearts. Then, diamond king to the ace and a second heart finesse will yield nine tricks. There are risks to this approach — for one thing, the heart finesse might lose — but other tries court even greater dangers.

SOLUTION 91

North
- ♠ J 7
- ♡ 3
- ◇ K 5 4 3
- ♣ A K Q 7 6 4

West
- ♠ 10 8 6 4 3 2
- ♡ A J 5
- ◇ 8
- ♣ J 9 3

East
- ♠ Q 9 5
- ♡ K 8 7
- ◇ Q 9 7 6
- ♣ 10 8 2

South
- ♠ A K
- ♡ Q 10 9 6 4 2
- ◇ A J 10 2
- ♣ 5

5◇ by South
Lead: ♠ 4

If diamonds break 4-1, dummy's shortage of entries will make it impossible to bring in the club suit when a ruff is needed to establish the suit. Therefore, declarer should concentrate on managing the play if trumps are 3-2 with clubs no worse than 4-2; or, if trumps are 4-1 with clubs 3-2.

One scheme, after winning the spade lead, is to begin by cashing the ace of diamonds. Suppose, first, that the queen of diamonds drops under the ace. Declarer can continue with the diamond jack, confirming the 4-1 split, let us say, then a club to the ace, a club ruff, and (if clubs are not wildly skewed) a diamond to dummy's king, followed by high clubs.

When the diamond ace collects only small cards, declarer can continue with the diamond jack, intending to run it if West follows low. When trumps are 3-2, declarer can maneuver to ruff a club and draw trumps from dummy (or have an extra trump in dummy for re-entry). When West has four trumps, declarer can draw three rounds, then play on clubs.

When East has four trumps to the queen, so that West shows out on the second round of trumps, declarer can go up with dummy's king of diamonds, cash the second high spade, and play clubs, hoping for a 3-3 break in that suit. When the clubs do divide, if East ever ruffs low declarer can overruff, and play a trump. If East ruffs high, then forces dummy to ruff, declarer can play more clubs, capturing East's remaining trump with the diamond ten while dummy still has a trump re-entry to any remaining clubs.

North
- ♠ A Q 10
- ♡ A Q J 10 6
- ♢ A 9 3
- ♣ A K

West
- ♠ J 6 3
- ♡ 9 8 7
- ♢ Q 10 6 5
- ♣ Q 9 5

East
- ♠ K 5 4 2
- ♡ 4 3 2
- ♢ 4
- ♣ 8 7 6 3 2

South
- ♠ 9 8 7
- ♡ K 5
- ♢ K J 8 7 2
- ♣ J 10 4

6NT by South
Lead: ♡9

The book safety play for four diamond tricks is to cash the ◇K, then lead a low diamond to dummy's nine. However, in books there are adequate entries to both hands. In real life, we are not always so lucky with our entries. Here, you cannot afford to take the classical safety play because if dummy's ◇9 were to lose to an honor, a heart continuation would deprive the closed hand of its last entry — bye bye diamonds.

If no perfect safety play against 4-1 diamond breaks is possible, how about the least imperfect one available? Declarer should begin by winning the heart king and leading the diamond eight, intending to let it ride. Several different things might happen. When diamonds are 3-2, or West has any singleton, or East has the singleton queen, declarer will easily get the tricks he requires from diamonds. When East has the singleton ten of diamonds, declarer will be sorry he was so clever.

When East has a small singleton diamond, and West ducks, declarer wins the diamond eight, then takes a spade finesse. Later, South runs his heart-club winners and tests diamonds (which, in effect, takes the second spade finesse, because West is squeezed; declarer also succeeds when East has king-jack-doubleton of spades). As declarer has secured three diamond tricks without losing any, the contract will come home if at least one of the spade finesses wins. Should West cover the diamond eight with the ten, declarer wins with dummy's ace, then leads the diamond nine, covering with the jack when East shows out. West has to duck that, else declarer gets four diamond tricks. So, declarer takes one spade finesse now, and another when he wins the king of diamonds.

SOLUTION 93

North
- ♠ 5 4 3
- ♡ K J 7 2
- ◇ 6 2
- ♣ A K 9 2

West
- ♠ K 9 6
- ♡ 9 5 4
- ◇ A K 9 8
- ♣ J 7 4

East
- ♠ J 2
- ♡ Q 10 8 6
- ◇ 5 4 3
- ♣ Q 10 8 3

South
- ♠ A Q 10 8 7
- ♡ A 3
- ◇ Q J 10 7
- ♣ 6 5

4♠ by South
Lead: ◇ K

There is little point in ruffing in dummy at Trick 3. If East can ruff only with the spade deuce, there is no hope for the contract (and it would surely have been doubled). Furthermore, that extra trump in dummy might come in handy when East has four trumps.

If East ruffs the third diamond, declarer is reduced to a spade finesse plus a break (a better chance than the double finesse). But what if he doesn't? Then, after winning the third diamond in the closed hand, declarer has these options: (a) double finesse in spades; (b) ace of spades, and a spade from dummy to the ten (in case East has king-jack-fourth); (c) the heart finesse to ditch the last diamond, then two finesses in spades; (d) finesse the spade queen.

The trouble with (a) is that, if the spade honors are split, West may win the first finesse and give East a diamond overruff. Line (b) is an improvement on (a). In the spade suit itself, it loses compared to (a) only when East has three spades to the king. If that is the spade position, declarer may lose a diamond overruff when he finesses the ten of spades. The same may happen when East has king-doubleton. If declarer should try the queen-finesse first, he may lose an overruff when East has two or three spades to the jack. Even if a diamond overruff were only a fifty-fifty proposition, (b), which does better against singleton and doubleton honors behind, would be indicated over (a). And the early play suggests that the chances are greater than that.

What about (c)? We don't like it. You need a finesse plus a decent heart break to begin with, and you're not out of the woods even then — there could be a red-suit uppercut when East holds a doubleton spade honor and West holds the spade nine.

Line (d) makes some sense. Line (b) has the danger that East, with king-doubleton of spades and four diamonds, will give West an overruff. The losing cases for (d), a simple overruff in situations such as the diagram, are only slightly more likely. All in all, a close question.

SOLUTION 94

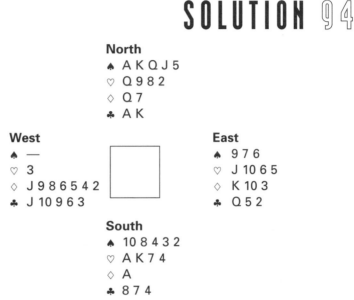

North
♠ A K Q J 5
♡ Q 9 8 2
◊ Q 7
♣ A K

West
♠ —
♡ 3
◊ J 9 8 6 5 4 2
♣ J 10 9 6 3

East
♠ 9 7 6
♡ J 10 6 5
◊ K 10 3
♣ Q 5 2

South
♠ 10 8 4 3 2
♡ A K 7 4
◊ A
♣ 8 7 4

7♣ by South
Lead: ♣J

Beware of tricky opponents! You should finish drawing trumps, then cash the king of clubs, and lead the heart nine to your ace. Now, (a) If both opponents follow low, ruff your last club high in dummy, and finish the spades, throwing a heart from dummy, hoping for a red-suit squeeze should hearts not divide favorably. (b) If West plays a heart honor under your ace, follow the same line as (a) being careful to make the heart discard from dummy the eight, in case a heart finesse is needed. (c) If East plays a heart honor when you lead to the heart ace, cash the heart king. Unless West shows out, you can claim. When West does show out, ruff a club high, and finish the trumps, throwing a heart from dummy. If East has the diamond king you will nail him in a criss-cross squeeze, in spite of his trickiness. In the diagram shown, check out what East's subtle heart play will do to you if you fail to clear the top club before cashing the second high heart. (It isn't necessary to take it immediately.)

SOLUTION 95

North
- ♠ J 10 5
- ♡ 8 7 3
- ◇ K 9 2
- ♣ K Q 6 4

West
- ♠ 9 8 7
- ♡ 9 4
- ◇ A 7 6
- ♣ J 9 8 7 2

East
- ♠ —
- ♡ K Q J 10 5
- ◇ Q J 10 8 5 3
- ♣ 10 5

South
- ♠ A K Q 6 4 3 2
- ♡ A 6 2
- ◇ 4
- ♣ A 3

6♠ by South
Lead: ♡9

Pitching a diamond on a winning club will leave you nothing useful to do for an encore. The only chance is to play West for the ace of diamonds. This is not terribly unlikely, since the nonvulnerable West might have sacrificed against your vulnerable slam if he had no sign of a defensive trick.

Granting West the ace of diamonds, and assuming from the bidding that he has the defensive club length, you know the contract is makable. You can squeeze West: win the lead, play all the trumps but one, and cash the club ace (for information), to produce this ending:

North
- ♠ —
- ♡ —
- ◇ K 9
- ♣ K Q 6

South
- ♠ 2
- ♡ 6 2
- ◇ 4
- ♣ 3

Suppose you lead the last trump. If West keeps fewer than three clubs, you throw a diamond from dummy and take three club tricks. Alternatively, if West keeps three clubs plus the ace of diamonds, you throw a club from dummy and lead a diamond. The problem with this squeeze is that you may have to guess the defenders' distributions.

We'd expect to get this distributional guess right almost always. Part of the time, the defenders will err (for example, West will throw a heart if he has one — it is now safe to lead towards the king of diamonds), or will attempt to conceal their holdings ineffectively. Anyway, declarer will go right almost all the time based on the bidding — West would probably have bid four notrump, not five clubs, with 4-4 or 4-5 in the minors. And with 3-1-3-6, West might have bid more.

SOLUTION 96

North
- ♠ A K
- ♡ K Q 7 6 4
- ◇ J 6 5 2
- ♣ 8 6

West
- ♠ J 9 3 2
- ♡ 5 3
- ◇ K 9
- ♣ Q J 10 4 3

East
- ♠ Q 10 4
- ♡ J 10 9 8
- ◇ 10 8
- ♣ K 9 7 5

South
- ♠ 8 7 6 5
- ♡ A 2
- ◇ A Q 7 4 3
- ♣ A 2

6◇ by South
Lead: ♣Q

Line 1. Club ace, spade to dummy, diamond to the queen, diamond ace, hearts. **Line 2.** Club ace, diamond ace. If the king doesn't drop, high hearts. Should East ruff the third heart, overruff, spade to dummy, heart ruff, spade, heart. **Line 3.** Club ace, hearts. Should East ruff the third heart, then: (3A) discard a club and later finesse in trumps; (3B) overruff, diamond ace, and continue as in Line 2.

Let's compare Lines 1 and 2. On those deals on which trumps are not 4-0, Line 1 is under 50%. It needs the diamond finesse onside, but still fails when East has king-third of diamonds and a singleton heart. In contrast, Line 2 is better than 50%. It makes (usually) when hearts are 3-3; when East has two hearts with one diamond; usually, when East has two hearts with two diamonds; much of the time when East has two hearts and three diamonds; when East has four hearts plus two or three small diamonds, or king singleton or tripleton in diamonds; and in several unlikely cases with wilder red-suit distributions.

Which is better, (3A) or (3B)? They differ only when East has two hearts. Then, (3A) gains occasionally when East has king-third of diamonds (because for (3B) to succeed, East must have at least three spades — he gets to discard a spade on the fourth round of hearts). However, (3B) succeeds and (3A) fails any time East has three small diamonds, and when East has two small diamonds with fewer than six spades. So, (3B) is superior to (3A). Finally, let's compare (2) with (3B). The two lines are equivalent when hearts are 3-3. When East has two hearts, they are almost equivalent — (2) is a tad better, because it gains when East has a small singleton diamond with his two little hearts. When East has four hearts, (3B) gains if he has king-doubleton of diamonds, but (2) gains in the same number of cases if East has two small diamonds. And (2) gains when East has king-third of diamonds with his four hearts — a tiny chance. Finally, (2) gains a bit more when hearts are 5-1 (or 6-0) — for example, the king of diamonds might be singleton. Final result: Line 2 is best, but not necessarily by enough to worry about.

SOLUTION 97

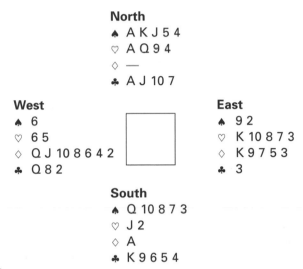

North
♠ A K J 5 4
♡ A Q 9 4
♢ —
♣ A J 10 7

West
♠ 6
♡ 6 5
♢ Q J 10 8 6 4 2
♣ Q 8 2

East
♠ 9 2
♡ K 10 8 7 3
♢ K 9 7 5 3
♣ 3

South
♠ Q 10 8 7 3
♡ J 2
♢ A
♣ K 9 6 5 4

6♠ by South
Lead: ♢ Q

You could plan to win the lead, draw trumps, and take the heart finesse. Should that lose, you can win the heart return, run hearts, and hope to get a count on clubs. That is a sensible plan, but you may not be able to get a complete count. Since the number of diamonds each opponent bid depends largely on that individual's idea of best strategy, West may have, for example, seven or eight diamonds to East's five or four. Being off by one diamond may be enough to cause you to get the clubs wrong.

A superior approach is to throw a heart from dummy on the first trick, planning to draw trumps, then play king and another club. If West shows out on the second club, go up with dummy's ace, then endplay East with a third round of clubs. Should West follow to the second round of clubs, ensure the contract by finessing, either picking up clubs or end-playing East with his doubleton club queen. This plan will fail only when West is void of clubs and lacks the heart king. Therefore, should West turn up with all three missing spades it might be superior to switch to the heart finesse, relying on guessing clubs should it fail.

SOLUTION 98

North
- ♠ A Q 10 9
- ♡ 8
- ◇ Q 7 5 4
- ♣ K 10 9 4

West
- ♠ K J 8 6 5
- ♡ Q J 10 9 7
- ◇ A 2
- ♣ 3

East
- ♠ 4 3 2
- ♡ A K 6 5 2
- ◇ 3
- ♣ J 8 7 6

South
- ♠ 7
- ♡ 4 3
- ◇ K J 10 9 8 6
- ♣ A Q 5 2

5◇ by South
Lead: ♣3

From the opening lead, it is not hard to see how West intends to defeat the contract. He has something resembling 5-5-2-1 distribution, so the defense is headed for two red-suit tops and a club ruff. When East has the ace of diamonds, there is nothing you can do to stop that ruff. Concentrate your energies on counter-measures that will be effective when West has the ace of trumps.

Then, it will be futile to drive out the ace of trumps early. You should plan to win the first trick in the closed hand so as to be in position to take the spade finesse. Then, spade to the queen, spade ace to pitch a heart, spade nine to pitch another heart if East plays low. Your hope is that West was dealt king-jack of spades, certainly a fair chance.

Watch out at Trick 1. Do not play the nine or ten of clubs from dummy. Let's see what happens if you should make that very human error. East ducks (he has nothing to gain by covering), and you must win with a closed-hand honor in order to execute your scissors coup in spades. Then, spade queen, spade ace to pitch a heart, spade ten to pitch another heart. You successfully avoid the club ruff, but now you have a club loser.

North
♠ A Q 6 5 2
♡ K 10 4 3
♢ A Q
♣ 8 7

West
♠ 4 3
♡ —
♢ 7 6 5 4 3 2
♣ J 10 9 5 2

East
♠ J 9 8 7
♡ J 9 7 6
♢ J 10 8
♣ K Q

South
♠ K 10
♡ A Q 8 5 2
♢ K 9
♣ A 6 4 3

6♡ by South
Lead: ♣J

There will be no problem unless trumps are 4-0. The North-South heart combination is one of a number of annoyances that bridge players have to put up with as part of the price of the beauty of the game. If you start with the heart king, you can pick up all four hearts in East, but not in West; if you start with the heart ace, you can do the reverse. There is, unfortunately, no way to guard against all possible heart divisions.

If picking up the heart suit without loss were the only consideration, there would be little to choose between the two approaches to playing hearts. In the actual case, however, there is a secondary consideration. If you misguess which opponent has four trumps, you are still in the ball game. You need to be able to run four spades without interference, to get rid of two losing clubs, then play the fifth spade while the defender uses up his trump trick. A 3-3 spade split will be of no avail in this situation. So, the correct line of play will be to finesse the ten on the first round of spades. When West has the long trumps, you will need to find him with four spades missing the jack; when East has the long trumps, you will need to find him with four spades including the jack. Since the spade jack is more likely to be with the long spades, the latter is more likely. Thus, you are more likely to survive misguessing trumps when East has four hearts. Therefore, the correct play is the heart ace at Trick 2.

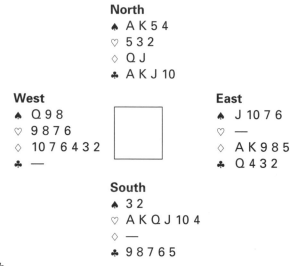

North
♠ A K 5 4
♡ 5 3 2
◇ Q J
♣ A K J 10

West
♠ Q 9 8
♡ 9 8 7 6
◇ 10 7 6 4 3 2
♣ —

East
♠ J 10 7 6
♡ —
◇ A K 9 8 5
♣ Q 4 3 2

South
♠ 3 2
♡ A K Q J 10 4
◇ —
♣ 9 8 7 6 5

6♡ by South
Lead: ◇ 4

This didn't look like a trump-control problem when it started, but things are often not what they seem at first glance. You cannot afford to leave trumps out — you might lose a club ruff and a club trick — so you must finish removing West's trumps. In order to overcome the club blockage you must discard a diamond from dummy on the last trump.

If you do that, the contract is safe. You continue with ace, king and another club. Even if clubs are 4-0, it can't help the opponents to hold up, since a fourth round of clubs unblocks the suit for you. Should East win the third round of clubs and punch out your last trump with a diamond, you discard dummy's blocking club to give life to two more clubs in your hand. (That's why you threw a diamond from dummy on the fourth round of hearts.)

Note that it is not quite good enough to throw a club on the third round of hearts. The 4-0 club break is then fatal. East lets you win the third round of clubs in dummy, and the clubs in your hand are dead — you have only eleven tricks.

More Bridge Titles from
Master Point Press

ABTA Book of the Year Award winners

25 Bridge Conventions You Should Know
by Barbara Seagram and Marc Smith (foreword by Eddie Kantar)
192pp., PB   Can $19.95   US$ 15.95

Eddie Kantar teaches Modern Bridge Defense
Eddie Kantar teaches Advanced Bridge Defense
by Eddie Kantar
each 240pp., PB Can $27.95   US$ 19.95

Interactive CD-ROM Editions

Modern Bridge Defense   Can $69.95, US$ 49.95
Advanced Bridge Defense   Can $69.95, US$ 49.95

The Bridge Technique Series
by David Bird & Marc Smith
each 64pp. PB, Can $7.95 US $5.95

Entry Management	Reading the Cards
Safety Plays	Tricks with Finesses
Tricks with Trumps	Planning in Defense
Eliminations and Throw Ins	Planning in Notrump Contracts
Deceptive Card Play	Defensive Signaling
Planning in Suit Contracts	Squeezes for Everyone

Around the World in 80 Hands by Zia Mahmood with David Burn
256pp., PB   Can $22.95   US $16.95

A Study in Silver *A second collection of bridge stories*
by David Silver
128pp., PB   Can $12.95   US$ 9.95

Becoming a Bridge Expert by Frank Stewart
300pp., PB   Can $27.95   US $19.95

The Best of Bridge Today Digest by Matthew and Pamela Granovetter
300pp., PB   Can $27.95   US $19.95

Bridge Problems for a New Millennium by Julian Pottage
212pp., PB   Can $19.95   US $14.95

Bridge the Silver Way by David Silver and Tim Bourke
192pp., PB   Can $19.95   US $14.95

Bridge: 25 Ways to Compete in the Bidding.
by Barbara Seagram and Marc Smith
220pp., PB   Can.$19.95   US $15.95

Bridge Squeezes for Everyone by David Bird
224pp., PB   Can $24.95   US $17.95

Bridge, Zia... and me by Michael Rosenberg
(foreword by Zia Mahmood)
192pp., PB   Can $19.95   US $15.95

Challenge Your Declarer Play by Danny Roth
128pp., PB   Can. $12.95   US $ 9.95

Classic Kantar a *collection of bridge humor* by Eddie Kantar
192pp., PB   Can $19.95   US $14.95

Competitive Bidding in the 21st Century by Marshall Miles
254pp.,PB   Can. $22.95   US. $16.95

Countdown to Winning Bridge by Tim Bourke and Marc Smith
92pp., PB   Can $19.95   US $14.95

Easier Done Than Said *Brilliancy at the Bridge Table*
by Prakash K. Paranjape
128pp., PB   Can $15.95   US $12.95

For Love or Money *The Life of a Bridge Journalist*
by Mark Horton and Brian Senior
189pp., PB   Can $22.95   US $16.95

Focus On Declarer Play by Danny Roth
128pp., PB   Can $12.95   US $9.95

Focus On Defence by Danny Roth
128pp., PB   Can $12.95   US $9.95

Focus On Bidding by Danny Roth
160pp., PB   Can $14.95   US $11.95

I Shot my Bridge Partner by Matthew Granovetter
384pp., PB   Can $19.95   US $14.95

Murder at the Bridge Table by Matthew Granovetter
320pp., PB   Can $19.95   US $14.95

Partnership Bidding a *workbook* by Mary Paul
96pp., PB   Can $9.95   US $7.95

Playing with the Bridge Legends by Barnet Shenkin
(forewords by Zia and Michael Rosenberg)
240pp., PB   Can $24.95   US $17.95

Saints and Sinners *The St. Titus Bridge Challenge*
by David Bird & Tim Bourke
192pp., PB   Can $19.95   US $14.95

Samurai Bridge *A tale of old Japan* by Robert F. MacKinnon
256pp., PB   Can $ 22.95   US $16.95

Tales out of School *'Bridge 101' and other stories* by David Silver
(foreword by Dorothy Hayden Truscott)
128pp., PB   Can $ 12.95   US $9.95

The Bridge Magicians by Mark Horton and Radoslaw Kielbasinski
248pp., PB   Can $24.95   US $17.95

The Bridge Player's Bedside Book edited by Tony Forrester
256pp., HC   Can $27.95   US $19.95

The Complete Book of BOLS Bridge Tips edited by Sally Brock
176pp., PB (photographs)   Can $24.95   US $17.95

The Pocket Guide to Bridge by Barbara Seagram and Ray Lee
64pp., PB   Can $9.95   US$7.95

There Must Be A Way... *52 challenging bridge hands*
by Andrew Diosy (foreword by Eddie Kantar)
96pp., PB $9.95 US & Can.

Thinking on Defense
by Jim Priebe
216pp., PB   Can $19.95   US$15.95

You Have to See This... *52 more challenging bridge problems*
by Andrew Diosy and Linda Lee
96pp., PB   Can $12.95   US $9.95

Win the Bermuda Bowl with Me by Jeff Meckstroth and Marc Smith
288pp., PB (photographs)   Can $24.95   US $17.95

World Class — *conversations with the bridge masters* by Marc Smith
288pp., PB (photographs)   Can $24.95   US $17.95